Oxford Secondary

science 2

Terry Jennings

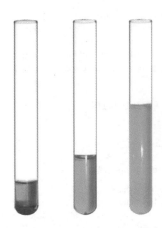

OXFORD
UNIVERSITY PRESS

OXFORD
UNIVERSITY PRESS

Great Clarendon Street, Oxford ox2 6DP

Oxford University Press is a department of the University of Oxford.
It furthers the University's objective of excellence in research, scholarship,
and education by publishing worldwide in

Oxford New York

Auckland Cape Town Dar es Salaam Hong Kong Karachi Kuala Lumpur
Madrid Melbourne Mexico City Nairobi New Delhi Shanghai Taipei Toronto

With offices in

Argentina Austria Brazil Chile Czech Republic France Greece
Guatemala Hungary Italy Japan Poland Portugal Singapore
South Korea Switzerland Turkey Ukraine Vietnam

Oxford is a registered trademark of Oxford University Press
in the UK and in certain other countries.

ISBN: 978-0-19-906063-4

Fourth Impression 2013

Acknowledgements

Photographs: p. 25: Boland Cell; p. 27: Abdul Wahid Khairi; pp. 44, 57, 58 (polar bear), 59 (cactus), 61 (trees), 63 (desert),
64 (sheep, cheetah), 125, 141, 143, 149, 151, 153, 157, 167, and 177–9: OUP Picture Bank, UK; pp. 107, 109–10, 112, and
146: Sophia/Ashish Andrew; p. 115: Fireman YU/iStockphoto;
p. 127 (hot plate): Elxeneize/Shutterstock and (thermal imaging camera): FLIR B50, FLIR Systems, Inc of Wilsonville, Oregon;
p. 128: Carla F. Castagno/Dreamstime.com; p. 134: Loskutnikov/Shutterstock; p. 136: Christina Tisi-Kramer/Shutterstock;
p. 137: Roy Dempsey/123rf; p. 172 (circuit-breaker): Savreen Kaur;
p. 175 (electromagnet): Dan Van Den Broeke/Dreamstime.com; p. 176: James Steidl/Shutterstock;
p. 187 (Ulysses): SOHO (ESA & courtesy NASA) and (dwarf star): courtesy NASA, ESA, H. Bond (STScI) and
M. Barstow (University of Leichester);
p. 191 (black hole): L. Ferrarese (Johns Hopkins University) and (white dwarf star): courtesy NASA; p. 192: Kruwt/Dreamstime.com;
p. 193 (Arecibo Radio Telescope): Israel Pabon/Shutterstock and (telescopes near Socorro): NRAO/AUI/NS

Printed in Pakistan at
Mas Printers, Karachi
Published by
Ameena Saiyid, Oxford University Press
No. 38, Sector 15, Korangi Industrial Area,
PO Box 8214, Karachi-74900, Pakistan

Introduction

Understanding science is vital if we are to understand the world in which we all live and work. Science is important to everyone—young or old, male or female, city or rural dweller. It is science that has brought our world to where it is today. Science has created the comforts we enjoy and the problems with which we must deal. Used wisely, science can make the world a better place; used unwisely it can lead to global disasters.

Science involves mental discipline and, as with many other things, students should be exposed to that mental discipline when they are young. Learning science helps us to think in a special way: to ask questions, test explanations through measurement or experiment, and to clarify our ideas. Those who do not learn to think in a scientific, systematic way may grow up blindly, accepting all they are told, confusing science with superstition, and reaching hasty judgements rather than considered opinions.

It is important to realise that science is not something done to us, for us, or at us by experts: it is something we participate in ourselves. Each one of us should know and understand enough science to keep abreast of developments that affect our lives. We should be able to use scientific skills to make intelligent decisions. Life in an advanced technological society is driven by scientific decision-making. Should we build more nuclear power plants? Which diseases should scientists spend huge sums of money studying? Is it safe to use genetically-engineered crops to increase food supplies? How do we deal with global warming? And an additional reason for learning science is that more scientists, technicians, and engineers will be needed to run the complex world of the future.

The *Oxford Secondary Science* series is designed to provide a straightforward approach to the teaching of science in the first three years of secondary education. It develops and extends the learning acquired in the primary school from courses such as *New Oxford Primary Science* by Nicholas Horsburgh, and *Science Success* and *Simply Science*, by Terry Jennings.

Oxford Secondary Science covers the requirements of the Pakistani National Curriculum for General Science 2006 at Grades VI, VII, and VIII. The series aims to meet the needs of teachers and students by building on and developing the core scientific themes studied in primary school in carefully graded stages, thereby providing a comprehensive introduction to science for students aged 11 to 14 years.

The course has been designed with four main aims:

1. To provide students with a solid body of knowledge of the natural, physical, and earth sciences.
2. To develop and extend students' knowledge and experience of scientific enquiry.
3. To enable students to explore values and attitudes through science.
4. To encourage students to think about how science can best be used.

These four elements are developed side by side through the books which make up the complete course.

Oxford Secondary Science is an interactive course, designed to provoke students to think, and it is flexible enough to meet the needs of students of all abilities. It also promotes the development of independent learning. For these reasons, *Oxford Secondary Science* will provide a scientific learning experience that is not only thorough, but at the same time, stimulating as well as exciting for teachers and students alike.

Terry Jennings

Contents

OXFORD
UNIVERSITY PRESS

LEARNING OUTCOMES

After studying this chapter students should be able to:

- describe the various components of the human digestive system
- describe digestion and its importance
- describe how various kinds of foods are digested
- identify common disorders of the digestive system
- list the factors that lead to constipation and diarrhoea, along with the measures that can be taken to prevent them

- describe the mechanism of respiration in humans
- differentiate between the two distinct processes of breathing and burning
- identify the common diseases of the respiratory system and discuss their causes, as well as preventive measures

- explain the transport system in humans
- describe the structure and function of the heart and blood vessels
- explain the working of the circulatory system
- identify scientific developments that provide alternatives for dysfunctional body parts such as artificial tissues and organs, and their transplantation
- understand that some disorders of the human transport system can be affected by diet

- describe the absorption of water in plants through the roots
- explain how the structure of the roots, stem, and leaves of a plant permit the movement of food, water, and gases

Contents

OXFORD
UNIVERSITY PRESS

LEARNING OUTCOMES

After studying this chapter students should be able to:

- define pollination
- compare self- and cross-pollination
- list various factors involved in cross-pollination
- differentiate between sexual and asexual reproduction
- describe fertilization
- describe the seed and fruit formation

- explain the term ecosystem
- define the term habitat
- compare different habitats
- describe various features that allow animals and plants to live in a particular habitat
- identify the factors that cause daily and yearly changes in a habitat
- explain how living things adapt to daily and yearly changes in their habitat

- explain the ways in which living things respond to changes in daily environmental conditions such as light intensity, temperature, and rainfall
- explain why food chains always begin with a producer
- illustrate the relationship between producers and consumers
- identify at least two food chains in the environment around them
- explain what a food web is

- describe the ways in which clean water is vital for meeting the needs of humans and other living things
- identify the sources of water
- identify substances present in water that make the water impure
- suggest different ways to clean impure water
- describe the various uses of water in our country
- investigate the consumption of water in our daily life and suggest ways to reduce wastage of water

- describe the structure of an atom
- differentiate between atomic number and mass number
- draw diagrams of the atomic structures of the first eighteen elements in the periodic table
- define valency
- explain the formation of ions
- differentiate between cations and anions

- describe isotopes and their uses in the field of medicines and agriculture
- identify the types and number of elements present in simple molecules and compounds
- write chemical formulae from a list of anions and cations
- state the law of constant composition and give examples

Contents

CHAPTER 9

PHYSICAL AND CHEMICAL CHANGES

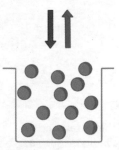

- To extend earlier learning regarding physical and chemical changes
- To identify examples of physical and chemical changes occurring in the environment
- To explain the importance of hydrocarbons as fuels
- To explain the physical and chemical properties of fertilizers, their uses, and harmful effects when misused
- To introduce simple ideas on the hydrogenation of vegetable oil into fat
- To introduce simple ideas on the manufacture, properties, and uses of plastics
- To compare and contrast reversible and non-reversible changes in a variety of materials and situations

CHAPTER 10

HEAT ON THE MOVE

- To explain that heat is a form of energy that is transferred from a region of higher temperature to one of lower temperature
- To explain conduction, convection, and radiation with the aid of practical examples
- To examine appliances that make use of the different modes of heat transfer
- To examine some examples of good and poor conductors of heat and their applications
- To explain the structure and functioning of a vacuum flask

CHAPTER 11

DISPERSION OF LIGHT

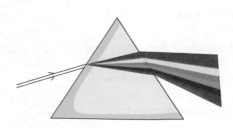

- To explain the causes of refraction of light and its effects
- To describe the dispersion of light by a prism and its effects
- To identify the primary colours and to demonstrate how they combine to form secondary colours
- To examine the uses of different coloured lights in the home, school, and wider environment
- To demonstrate, practically, how the colours of the rainbow can be recombined to form white light
- To explain the absorption and reflection of light by different objects and materials

LEARNING OUTCOMES

After studying this chapter students should be able to:

103

- differentiate between a physical and a chemical change
- identify some physical and chemical changes taking place in the environment
- explain the use of hydrocarbons as fuels
- explain the physical and chemical properties of fertilizers, which make them useful in agriculture
- discuss the harmful effects of misuse of fertilizers
- describe the chemical process by which vegetable oil changes into fat
- describe the simple process for the manufacture of plastics
- distinguish between the reversible and non-reversible changes in materials
- identify a variety of reversible and non-reversible changes in materials found in their surroundings

118

- explain the flow of heat from a hot body to a cooler body
- explain conduction, convection, and radiation through experimentation
- recognize the three modes of transfer of heat from the environment
- explain how birds can glide in the air for hours
- identify examples of appliances that make use of the different modes of transfer of heat
- identify heat-conducting materials in their surroundings
- describe the working and principle of the vacuum flask
- explain how a vacuum flask reduces the transfer of heat

131

- explain refraction of light and its causes
- discuss the effects of refraction with examples
- identify the colours of light using a prism
- describe the dispersion of light by a prism
- identify different uses of lights of different colours at home, school, and in the country. Also, explain the relationship of the choice of colours to their purpose
- define the spectrum of light
- identify primary colours and show how they can be combined to form secondary colours
- identify a device in their surroundings that uses different combinations of colours
- demonstrate how the spinning of a rainbow-coloured disc results in it appearing white
- explain why an opaque or non-luminous object appears to be of a certain colour

CHAPTER 12

SOUND WAVES

- To extend earlier learning regarding sound with an explanation of wavelength, frequency, and amplitude
- To examine examples of everyday objects that produce different sounds
- To compare and contrast the audible frequency range of humans with that of the other animals
- To identify the parts of musical instruments which vibrate and to explain the relationship between the shapes of instruments and the sounds they produce
- To examine the production and uses of sounds in everyday life

CHAPTER 13

CIRCUITS AND ELECTRIC CURRENTS

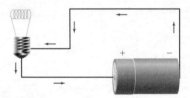

- To extend earlier learning with an explanation of what a current is and a comparison of the construction as well as uses of parallel and series circuits
- To explain the differences between current and energy, and to examine methods of measuring both
- To explain the relationship between voltage and resistance, along with the advantages and disadvantages of resistance
- To examine the effects of current in some of the everyday appliances
- To examine the major uses of electricity in the home
- To discuss potential hazards in the transmission and use of electricity, and to examine the safe use of electricity in the home, school as well as the wider environment

CHAPTER 14

INVESTIGATING SPACE

- To provide a simple explanation of the Big Bang Theory of the origin of the universe
- To examine the evidence for the Big Bang Theory
- To compare and contrast stars and other bodies in space that emit and reflect light
- To examine the structure and function of the Sun and ways of studying the Sun
- To explain galaxies and constellations and to identify the major constellations visible in the night sky
- To explain black holes and their formation
- To explain the structure and uses of telescopes in astronomy

GLOSSARY

OXFORD
UNIVERSITY PRESS

LEARNING OUTCOMES

After studying this chapter students should be able to:

- explain wavelength, frequency, and amplitude of sound and give their units
- state factors on which sound depends
- identify objects in the home and surroundings that are designed and made to produce different sounds
- compare the audible frequency range of humans and different animals
- design a musical instrument to explain the relationship between its shape and the sound it produces
- identify the applications of different sounds in daily life

- define current
- make parallel and series circuits
- investigate types of circuits used for different purposes
- identify a disadvantage of a series circuit
- differentiate between current and energy
- explain the effects of electric current in commonly used appliances
- describe voltage

- explain resistance as opposition to the flow of current
- describe the relationship between voltage and resistance
- measure current using different devices
- list the major uses of electricity in the home
- list electrical hazards and precautionary measures to ensure the safe use of electricity in the home
- explain why electricity is dangerous to humans

- explain the Big Bang Theory of the origin of the universe
- describe a star using properties such as brightness and colour
- identify bodies in space that emit and reflect light
- suggest safety methods to use when observing the Sun
- define the terms star, galaxy, Milky Way, and the black holes
- describe types of galaxies
- explain the birth and death of our Sun
- evaluate the evidence that supports scientific theories of the origin of the universe
- identify major constellations visible in the night sky
- describe the formation of black holes
- explain the working of a telescope

OXFORD
UNIVERSITY PRESS

CHAPTER 1

The digestive system

All the food we eat falls into five basic categories:

Carbohydrates such as sugars and starches, give us energy.

Proteins are body-building foods that are part of every cell in your body. They are also needed to repair damaged parts of the body.

Fats are stored as a layer of insulation under the skin. Fat produces twice as much energy per gram as carbohydrates and about a quarter of the energy we use each day comes from fats.

Minerals describe a whole collection of elements, including calcium and phosphorus, needed to build bones and teeth, sodium and potassium to keep nerves functioning properly, and tiny quantities of other minerals that help to keep us healthy.

Vitamins are essential to your health, but again, are only needed in tiny quantities. A lifetime's supply of all the vitamins you need only weighs about 250 g.

For a healthy diet, we also need fibre as to help the passage of food through the digestive system, and water to help dissolve the food and to make up for the water the body loses when breathing, sweating, excreting, etc.

BASIC FACTS

- Food has to be digested before it can be used by the body.
- Digestion is the breakdown of large molecules in the food into smaller molecules, which can be absorbed into the blood.
- Digestion is speeded up by chemicals called enzymes.
- In the mouth, the food is chewed and an enzyme in the saliva begins the digestion of starch (a carbohydrate) into simple sugars.
- In the stomach, proteins are digested with the help of hydrochloric acid and an enzyme.
- In the small intestine, starch, proteins, and fats are digested into simpler, small molecules with the help of several enzymes.
- During digestion, starch is broken down into glucose, maltose, and other simple sugars, proteins are broken down into amino acids, and fats are broken down into fatty acids and glycerol.
- The small molecules of digested food are absorbed into the bloodstream in the small intestine, with the help of the villi. Vitamins and mineral salts may also be absorbed in the small intestine.
- In the large intestine, most of the water and remaining mineral salts are absorbed from the undigested food into the bloodstream.
- The undigested food is stored in the rectum, before being passed out of the body through the anus.
- Indigestion is usually caused by eating food too quickly and not chewing it enough.
- Diarrhoea results from germs getting into the food.
- Constipation is caused by not eating enough fibre, not drinking enough water and other liquids, or not going to the lavatory at the usual time.

Large molecules

Everything you eat is made of molecules, but the molecules found in carbohydrates, fats, and proteins are large molecules. They have to be taken to every part of the body by the blood system. But because these energy-giving and body-building foods are large molecules, it is impossible for them to enter the blood vessels as they are.

Your digestive system is basically a tube 10 metres long which begins in the mouth and ends at the anus. The only way that carbohydrates, fats, and proteins can pass through the walls of this tube into the blood vessels is if they are made into smaller molecules. The process of breaking down food into smaller molecules is known as digestion.

Digestion

The digestive process involves:

- A mechanical breaking down of the food, e.g. by chewing it.

- A chemical break down of the food using acids and chemicals known as enzymes. Enzymes speed up the chemical reactions of digestion. They can carry out only one job. Enzymes which break down starch cannot break down fats or proteins.

- Absorption of the small molecules that the body can use.

- Removal of the insoluble waste materials from the body.

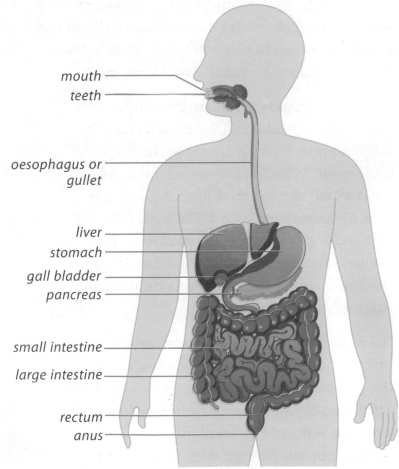

mouth
teeth
oesophagus or gullet
liver
stomach
gall bladder
pancreas
small intestine
large intestine
rectum
anus

The human digestive system

The digestive system

The digestive system is a long tube, much of it coiled up, which is 10 metres long. The human digestive system is shown in the diagram above.

The digestive process

The first part of the digestive process is **quick**—chewing the food into small pieces before it is swallowed. The food is mixed with saliva (or spit) which contains an enzyme called amylase. Amylase starts to break down starch in the food into a type of soluble sugar called maltose.

The chewed food is pushed down the **gullet** or **oesophagus** by waves of muscular contraction, like a series of squeezes, until it reaches the stomach. Food will go from your mouth to your stomach, even if you stand on your head.

Food is stored in the stomach for a few hours. The stomach can hold about 1.5 litres of food. The food is mixed with **gastric juice**, which is made by the walls of the stomach. Gastric juice contains hydrochloric acid, which kills most bacteria in the food. It also gives the best conditions for enzymes, called **proteases**, to begin breaking down proteins in the food. The food is churned around in the stomach for up to six hours after a large meal.

Food is slowly squashed and squeezed along the **small intestine,** at about 2.5 cm a minute. The small intestine is 7 metres long and about 3 cm in diameter. As the food is pushed through from the stomach into the small intestine, a little at a time, **bile** is squirted onto it. Bile is made by the liver and is stored in the gall bladder until it is needed. Bile emulsifies (breaks up) fats. It is also alkaline to make the conditions right for the enzymes in the small intestine.

The walls of the small intestine produce enzymes which digest proteins, carbohydrates, and fats. The **pancreas** produces three more enzymes which also digest proteins, carbohydrates, and fats. The walls of the small intestine are not smooth but are covered with millions of tiny finger-like projections called **villi**. The villi are perfect for absorbing food because they give the small intestine a much larger surface area. They have a thin outer layer of cells and a dense network of blood capillaries.

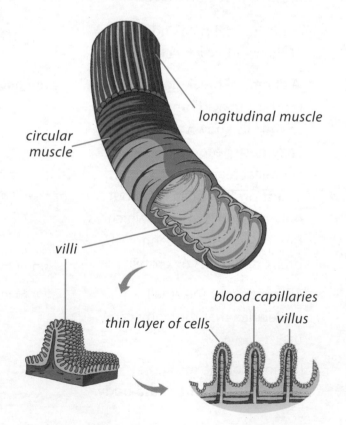

Part of the wall of the small intestine showing the villi

OXFORD
UNIVERSITY PRESS

The small molecules

By the time the food is digested, the large molecules of carbohydrates, proteins, and fats have been broken down into smaller molecules like this:

starch —— *carbohydrase enzymes* ——→ glucose and other simple sugars, e.g. maltose

proteins —— *protease enzymes* ——→ amino acids

fats —— *lipase enzymes* ——→ fatty acids and glycerol

Absorption

Nearly all of the absorption of the food into the blood system takes place in the small intestine. The digested foods are transported to the liver and the liver controls what happens to them:

- Glucose is needed for respiration. A constant supply of glucose circulates in the blood. If there is too much glucose, the liver converts some into insoluble glycogen. This can be changed back into glucose when it is needed.

- Excess carbohydrates are converted into fats.

- Amino acids, formed by the digestion of proteins, cannot be stored. They are used for the growth and repair of the body. Excess amino acids are changed to a substance called urea, which is then excreted.

In the large intestine, water and mineral salts are removed from the undigested food and absorbed into the blood. Food often contains cellulose (from plant cell walls) which we cannot digest. This and any remaining undigested material is passed on to the rectum where it is stored as **faeces** until it is passed out of the anus. About two-thirds of the faeces is water and about half of the rest is bacteria, mainly dead bacteria. The bacteria line the intestines and scientists believe they may play an important part in producing certain vitamins and helping the body to fight disease.

Problems with the digestive system

Germs get into the digestive system when you eat infected food. This is called food poisoning. Foods can be infected when you buy them, or while they are being prepared at home. Not washing the hands before preparing food and after using the toilet, dirty work surfaces and utensils, loose hanging hair, and sneezing near food can all lead to germs getting into food.

Indigestion

Indigestion is usually caused by eating food too quickly and not chewing it enough. The stomach produces extra gastric juice, with the result that the stomach contains a lot of acid. If the person belches, some of the acid comes up the gullet, causing a burning sensation, which is sometimes called 'heartburn'. Indigestion can usually be cured by taking a tablet or drink which contains an alkali that will neutralise the acid. A person who constantly has too much acid in his stomach may get an ulcer. This is when the acid starts to eat into the wall of the stomach, which then becomes raw and painful. Ulcers seem to be most common in middle-aged and elderly people, and often seem to be brought on by overwork and worry.

Diarrhoea

Infected food can be vomited from the stomach quite soon after it is eaten. More often, the germs are busy breeding and multiplying in your digestive system before you begin to feel ill. White blood cells rush to destroy the germs and the liquid food is rushed through the digestive system and out of the rectum. You can see why diarrhoea is often called 'the runs'.

Diarrhoea stops when the infection clears up. During the attack, a great deal of water and important mineral salts and vitamins may be lost. Diarrhoea is a serious illness in babies as they quickly become dehydrated (dried out) and ill. The lost water must be replaced and the baby taken to a doctor if the diarrhoea lasts more than a day. Extra hygiene is very important, otherwise the infection can spread to other people in the house.

Constipation

Part of the food you eat, including the fibre, cannot be broken down by the digestive system. It travels to the rectum where it forms faeces. The faeces are passed out of the anus by powerful muscles. People have very different lavatory habits. Some people go four times a day, once a day, every four days—or anything in between.

If faeces are not passed out according to your usual pattern, they may become thick, hard, and dry. This is because the waste stays in the large intestine for longer and has more than the usual amount of water absorbed from it. The thick, hard, and dry faeces are uncomfortable or even painful to pass.

Constipation is not serious and worry can make it worse. It is important to go to the toilet at the same time each day and when you have plenty of time. If nothing happens after, say, ten minutes do not worry. Try again the next day. Drink up to three litres of water a day and make sure you have enough fibre in your diet. This improves the tone of the muscles of the rectum and keeps the faeces bulky and soft. Make sure you have plenty of exercise since there is no better way to improve muscle tone. Try to avoid laxatives. These are medicines to soften the faeces. They work, but there is a risk that they may cause the powerful muscles of the rectum to lose their muscle tone and become lazy. You then need even stronger laxatives to help you to go to the lavatory.

OXFORD
UNIVERSITY PRESS

1. Name the seven groups of food that are needed for a healthy and balanced diet.

2. What is meant by 'digestion' and where does it occur?

3. Look at the diagram of the digestive system. Write down the names of the parts.

4. Why do we need to digest our food? What are the two ways in which food is broken down during digestion?

5. What two jobs are done by the saliva?

6. Glucose molecules do not have to be digested. Starch molecules do. Explain this difference.

7. Name the three nutrients which are broken down during digestion and say what they are broken down into.

8. Give three reasons why the villi in the small intestine are perfect for absorbing food.

9. What is the name of the organ that produces bile to break down fats?

10. What part do muscles play in digestion?

11. Our bodies cannot digest fibre (cellulose). Why is it still important in our diet?

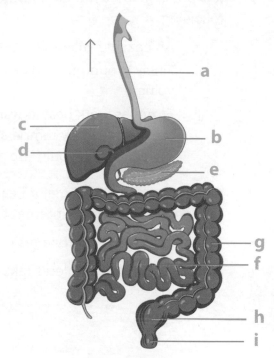

The digestive system

12. You ate a chicken sandwich for lunch. The bread contains mainly starch, while the butter is mostly fat. The chicken is mainly protein. Describe how this chicken sandwich is being digested so that the nutrients in it can be useful to your body.

13. What are the most likely causes of constipation? What can you do to reduce the chances that you will become constipated. How can constipation be cured?

14. What are the most likely causes of diarrhoea? What can you do to reduce the chances that you will get diarrhoea? How can diarrhoea be cured?

Things to do

1. Chew a piece of dry bread for a minute or two without swallowing it. What do you noticeabout the change in taste and texture of the bread? Explain your observations.

2. It is possible to buy dried enzymes. Devise an experiment that will prove the following:

   i.   An enzyme will only digest one type of food.

   ii. Finely ground food digests faster than large solid lumps with the same volume.

   iii. Enzymes work best in warm conditions (e.g. around 20°C) but most enzymes are destroyed by temperatures above 60°C. Describe what equipment and materials you would use and how you will record your results.

3. Obesity is becoming a major health problem in many western countries. Use reference books or the internet to find out what obesity is and what causes it.

4. Try to find out why herbivores can use grass as a food, but humans cannot.

5. Find out why some athletes take glucose tablets before a race.

OXFORD
UNIVERSITY PRESS

Respiration and energy from food

In most living organisms, including humans, the **energy** for life comes from a chemical reaction between food and oxygen. This reaction is called **aerobic respiration**. Aerobic means in the 'presence of air or oxygen'. You can live for a few days without food, but without air, you will die in a few minutes. It is the oxygen in the air which is so vital to you.

Sometimes, though, your breathing cannot get enough oxygen to your cells. If you are running a race, your muscles may need to release more energy for movement, but oxygen cannot get to your cells fast enough. The body gets this energy by breaking glucose down, without oxygen, into a substance called lactic acid. Energy is released and so you can carry on running. However, the lactic acid builds up in your muscles, causing your muscles to feel tired and eventually you may get painful cramp—it all depends on how fit you are! After the exercise you usually gasp for air taking in lots of oxygen. Your heart will also beat faster to get more oxygen to the cells. The lactic acid is slowly broken down into carbon dioxide and water. Only when all the lactic acid has been broken down, do your heart rate and breathing return to normal. Since this process releases energy from food without oxygen, it is called **anaerobic respiration**.

BASIC FACTS

- Breathing is the movement of air passing in and out of the lungs.
- Breathing involves the movement of the ribs and a large sheet of muscle, called the diaphragm, which stretches horizontally under the ribs across the body.
- The rate of breathing changes according to the needs of the body.
- The exchange of oxygen and carbon dioxide takes place in the millions of air sacs or alveoli, found inside the lungs. The oxygen is required by all cells in the body.
- Respiration is the process by which energy is released from food.
- Respiration is a chemical process which takes place in the cells.
- Oxygen is needed for aerobic respiration.
- The oxygen is carried around the body by the blood and used by the cells for their respiration.
- Carbon dioxide is a waste product of respiration and has to be taken to the lungs for removal.
- The air breathed out is warmer and contains less oxygen, but more water vapour and carbon dioxide than the air breathed in.
- Not all the oxygen is removed from the air breathed in.
- Coughs and colds are diseases of the respiratory system caused by viruses.
- Smoking tobacco damages the respiratory system and can cause diseases such as lung cancer and bronchitis.

Aerobic respiration involves three processes in the human body:

- Oxygen is taken to the cells of the body by the blood.

- Energy is released by the reaction of the dissolved food with oxygen.

- Carbon dioxide and water are taken back to be breathed out into the air.

In order to respire, the body first requires a supply of oxygen. Oxygen is obtained from the air that you breathe in through your mouth and nose.

The air that you breathe in passes down the windpipe or trachea. On the way, the air goes through the voice box or larynx. This is a box with walls made of gristle or cartilage. It contains thin membranes called vocal cords. When you speak, air passes over these vocal cords in a way which makes them vibrate and produce sounds.

The windpipe branches into two tubes, called bronchi, each of which is attached to a lung. Each bronchus splits up into smaller and smaller branches, called bronchioles. Eventually each microscopic branch ends in a microscopic air-sac. These air-sacs are called alveoli. Each lung contains millions of alveoli, so that the whole lung is like a huge sponge.

Every alveolus has a very large surface area which is very thin and moist. The alveoli are pink in colour because each is surrounded by blood capillaries.

Some of the oxygen from the air breathed in dissolves in the moisture on the surface of the alveoli and passes through their thin walls into the blood capillaries.

The parts of the human respiratory system

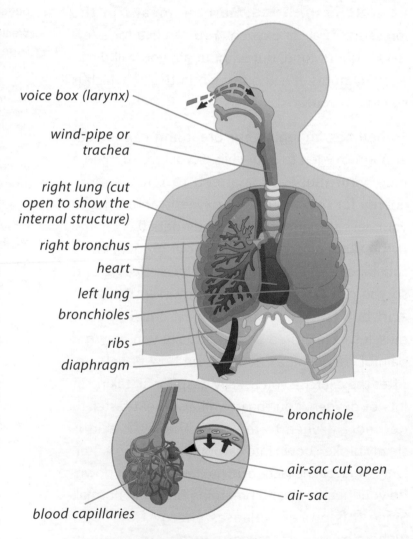

voice box (larynx)

wind-pipe or trachea

right lung (cut open to show the internal structure)

right bronchus

heart

left lung

bronchioles

ribs

diaphragm

bronchiole

air-sac cut open

air-sac

blood capillaries

Bronchiole and air-sacs (magnified)

At the same time, carbon dioxide passes from the blood capillaries into the alveoli. Eventually the carbon dioxide is breathed out of the body.

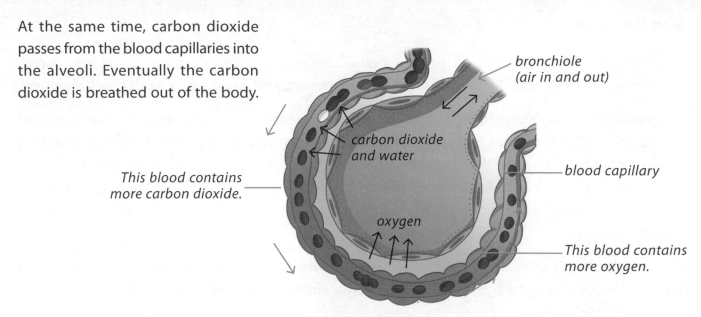

The exchange of gases in the alveoli

Respiration

Every cell in the body requires oxygen and food. Oxygen is carried around the body in the blood system. Once it has reached the cells where it is needed, it can react with the food molecules produced by digestion to produce energy. Water and carbon dioxide are produced at the same time. The following equation summarises the process of respiration.

food + oxygen ⟶ carbon dioxide + water + energy

After respiration has occurred, blood returning from the cells contains extra water and carbon dioxide and very little oxygen. The only way the carbon dioxide can be removed from the body is in the blood via the heart to the lungs. From there it is breathed out through the mouth and nose.

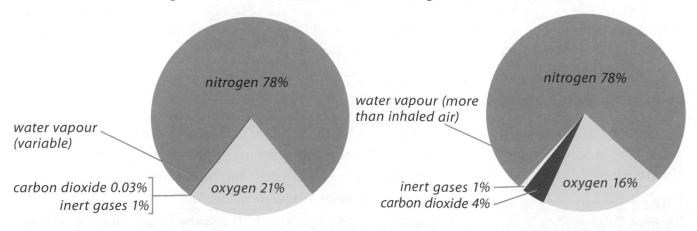

Composition of air inhaled by a person   **Composition of air exhaled by a person**

How we breathe

Breathing is different from many of the body's other actions. We can alter how quickly or how deeply we breathe for a short time. But as soon as we stop thinking about it, our breathing goes back to normal.

When we breathe, our chest changes shape. These movements are brought about by movements of the ribs and **diaphragm**. The diaphragm is a tough, dome-shaped sheet of muscle across the bottom of the chest. It helps to make the chest into an air-tight box. Both the ribs and diaphragm are moved by muscles. Each pair of ribs has muscles, called **intercostal muscles**, between them. Together, the intercostal muscles and the muscles of the diaphragm can make the volume of the chest cavity larger or smaller.

When we breathe in, or inhale, the diaphragm is pulled down and the rib cage is pulled upwards. The space inside the chest gets bigger. Air rushes into the lungs to try to fill up the extra space.

When we breathe out, or exhale, the muscles relax. The diaphragm moves upwards and the rib cage is lowered. The space in the chest gets smaller and air is forced out of the lungs.

Making the air moist, warm, and clean

You can see from the diagram on page 10, that it is possible for air to enter the lungs through either the mouth or nose. It is always best to breathe in through the nose. This is because germs and dust particles are filtered out by the hairs inside the nose and nasal cavity. The air is also warmed by the blood vessels in the nose and moistened by the slimy mucus produced by its lining. The air is further warmed by the many blood vessels that line the nasal cavity. Any dust and germs that are in the air you have breathed in, get caught in the mucus and are wafted towards the throat by tiny hairs called **cilia**, that protects the nasal passageways and other parts of the respiratory tract. If you breathe in through the mouth, dirty, dry, cold air can enter your lungs.

The windpipe (trachea), bronchi, and bronchioles are all lined with cells. Some of these cells produce mucus, which moistens the air as it is breathed in. The blood vessels around the windpipe, bronchi, and bronchioles carry warm blood. This warms the air. Oxygen in the warm moist air can then pass through the air sacs more easily.

As the lungs are such vital organs, they must be kept clean. Some of the cells lining the air tubes have small hairs sticking out into the tubes. These cilia are always moving. They move in waves like a brush. The movement of the cilia sweeps mucus and any remaining dust and germs towards the mouth. The dirty mucus can be blown out of the nose into a handkerchief or tissue. Any mucus that gets into the throat is coughed up, or swallowed when it goes to the stomach. There, the acid in the stomach kills any germs present.

OXFORD
UNIVERSITY PRESS

Diseases of the respiratory system

Coughs and colds

A cough is a sudden clearing of the air passages. But coughing, together with sneezing and a blocked or runny nose, are signs that you have a cold. Colds are caused by viruses which invade the cells lining the nose and throat, causing them to break down. This gives you a sore throat and runny nose. As yet there is no cure for a cold, although some medicines can relieve some of the effects of the cold. If you are healthy, your body will quite quickly overcome the cold viruses. Eating a healthy balanced diet, getting plenty of sleep and fresh air will all help. Use a tissue or handkerchief to stop the viruses being shot into the air and infecting other people.

Influenza or 'flu'

Influenza is caused by a virus, although it is a different virus from the one that causes colds, even though some of the symptoms are similar. The 'flu' virus enters the body through the eyes, nose, or mouth and travels down towards the lungs. Once the virus is in the windpipe, bronchi, and bronchioles, it keeps on multiplying. The first symptoms are a runny nose, sore throat, and cough. As the body tries to overcome the virus, it releases substances to try to fight it. These cause problems elsewhere in the body, including aching muscles, headaches, fever, and weakness. As with colds, there are medicines to relieve the symptoms of influenza, but no real cure. There are vaccines that can be injected to try to protect people against influenza, but the problem is that the virus keeps changing and it is impossible to produce vaccines quickly enough to fight each new form of the virus. As with colds, influenza may make you sneeze—it is your body's way of trying to get rid of the viruses that made you ill. But the average sneeze will spread over 100,000 viruses up to 10 metres, therefore, always use a tissue or handkerchief so that you do not infect everyone around you!

Asthma

Asthma is a disease in which the muscles in the bronchi contract, making it difficult for air to reach the lungs. One form of asthma treatment is to use an inhaler. This contains a drug that relaxes the muscles of the bronchi, making it easier to breathe. All sorts of things seem to be able to bring on an asthma attack. Dogs and cats cause asthma attacks in some people. Tobacco smoke, cold air, exercise, and even laughing can cause attacks. Worry and stress can make asthma attacks worse. Really bad attacks which force people to go into hospital often happen after a virus infection of the nose or chest. Some people get asthma from dust or fumes at work. However, there is no strong evidence to link asthma to air pollution. Of course, other things help to decide whether you get asthma in the first place—not just one attack, but the disease as a whole. You can inherit the tendency to develop asthma from one or both of your parents.

Smoking tobacco

Some of the worst, and avoidable, diseases of the respiratory system result from smoking tobacco. More than 300 different chemicals have been found in cigarette smoke. They include a drug called nicotine. This drug is **addictive** and speeds up the heart beat, and narrows the arteries, so causing high blood pressure. Also in tobacco smoke is tar. This coats the lining of the lungs and makes them less able to take in oxygen. The tar contains chemicals that can cause lung cancer. Smokers are about fourteen times more likely to die from lung cancer than non-smokers. Tobacco smoke also contains the poisonous gas carbon dioxide. This joins up with the red blood cells, stopping them from carrying oxygen around the body.

The first effects of tobacco smoke are that the bronchioles narrow and the cilia lining the air passages stop beating. The smoke also makes the lining of the air passages produce more mucus. This collects in the bronchioles, causing a 'smoker's cough'. With prolonged smoking, some of the substances in tobacco weaken the walls of the alveoli. The incessant 'smoker's cough' may eventually burst some of the weakened alveoli. In time, the absorbing surface of the lungs is greatly reduced. Then the smoker cannot oxygenate his blood properly. The damaged alveoli, and the effects of the carbon monoxide, can make the smoker breathless and exhausted at the slightest exertion. This disease is known as emphysema.

Another effect of cigarette smoke is that when the cilia in the air passages stop beating, and the excess mucus collects in the bronchi, the breathing tubes become inflamed. This inflammation is known as bronchitis. Over 95 per cent of the people suffering from bronchitis are smokers and they have a 20 times greater chance of dying from bronchitis than non-smokers.

Even if you do not smoke yourself, there are still risks from tobacco. It has been shown that repeated breathing in of smoke from a nearby smoker, known as 'passive smoking', can also damage your health.

Questions

1. What is the difference between breathing and respiration?

2. In which parts of living organisms does respiration take place?

3. Burning and respiration both use oxygen and both produce energy. Make a table to show the similarities and differences between burning and respiration.

4. Why do you breathe faster and your heart rate increases when you run?

5. Make a list of all the parts of the body that air flows through on its way to the lungs.

6. Explain the part played by the diaphragm and the intercostal muscles in breathing.

7. Why is it better to breathe through your nose than through your mouth?

8. Here is a diagram of the chest and lungs. In your notebook, label the parts of the diagram.

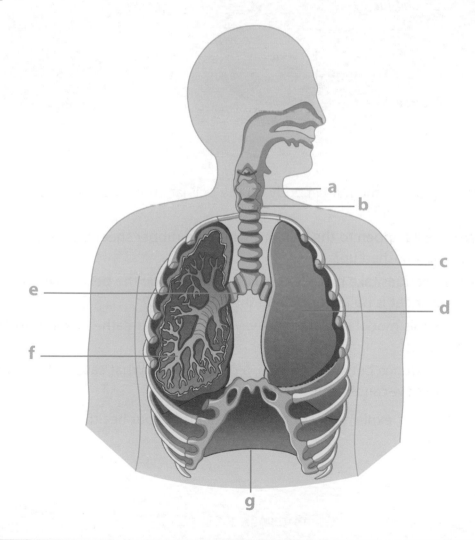

9. Here is a model of the chest and lungs. This model is often used to show how we breathe in and out:

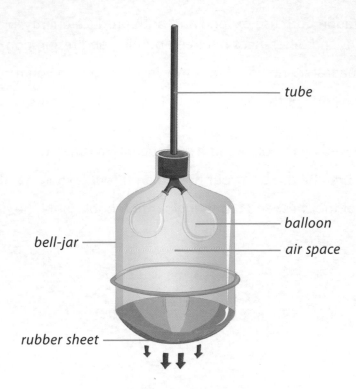

tube

balloon

bell-jar

air space

rubber sheet

i.   What parts of the human body do the bell-jar, tubing, balloons, and rubber sheet represent?

ii. What will happen to the balloons when the rubber sheet is pulled down and then pushed up?

iii. What changes take place to the air pressure inside the bell-jar when the rubber sheet is pulled down and then pushed up?

iv. How is this model similar to the way in which we breathe in and out? How is it different?

10. What is the difference between a cough, a cold, and flu? What causes these three conditions and how can they be prevented?

11. In your own words, explain why smoking can damage your health.

OXFORD
UNIVERSITY PRESS

Things to do

1. When you yawn you take a deep breath in and then let the air out quickly. Use reference books, or the internet, to help you explain each of the following in terms of breathing in and out: a cough; a gasp; a sneeze; a sigh; a laugh.

2. Use reference books, or the internet, to find out what artificial respiration is, why it is sometimes necessary, and how it is carried out. Why do scientists not like the words 'artificial respiration'?

3. Ask a butcher to show you the lungs of an animal. Identify the trachea and bronchi. If one lung has been cut open, look for the bronchioles. Can you explain why the lungs are red and spongy?

    SAFETY: If you touch the lungs, make sure you wash your hands thoroughly afterwards, especially before you touch food.

4. A friend of yours is going climbing in the Himalayas. The air pressure at the top of the mountains will be very low. There will not be as much oxygen. Write a letter explaining why you think it will be more difficult or easier for your friend to hold his or her breath on top of the mountains.

5. Make a pie graph showing the composition of air.

6. Use reference books, or the internet, to find out what is meant by 'passive smoking'. Write a short paragraph describing your findings.

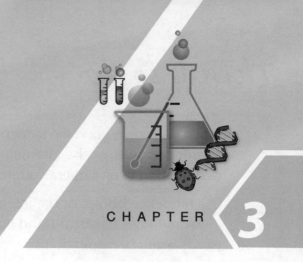

The human transport system

CHAPTER 3

BASIC FACTS

- The blood is a liquid tissue which consists of red blood cells, white blood cells, platelets, and plasma.
- Red blood cells contain haemoglobin which carries oxygen to the body cells.
- White blood cells engulf germs which get into the body and also produce antibodies.
- Platelets help the blood to clot and stop bleeding.
- Plasma, the liquid part of the blood, carries dissolved food, waste materials (urea and carbon dioxide), hormones and antibodies, as well as heat energy.
- The circulatory system transports wanted chemicals and waste chemicals around the body.
- The circulatory system is made up of the heart, arteries, veins, and capillaries.
- The heart is a muscular pump which circulates the blood round the body.
- Blood goes through the heart twice in one complete circulation of the body.
- Arteries carry blood away from the heart.
- Because the blood is under pressure, arteries have thick walls.
- When blood reaches the cells, arteries divide into millions of thin-walled capillaries.
- Food and oxygen pass from the capillaries into the cells. At the same time, waste chemicals pass from the cells into the capillaries.
- The capillaries then join together to form veins which carry blood back to the heart.
- Blood returns to the heart in veins.
- Veins have valves to stop the back-flow of blood, and muscular pressure makes the blood flow through the veins to the heart.
- The blood prevents infection by healing wounds and destroying invading germs.

If your body is to keep working properly, food, oxygen, water, and heat have to be carried from one place to another. Carbon dioxide and other waste chemicals have to be carried away for the body to be got rid of. Blood carries these things. It flows through blood vessels carrying the different things around your body. Your blood circulation does the same job as the road network with trucks on it. Of course, the blood does not move around on its own. That is where the heart comes in. The heart's job is to pump blood through the various blood vessels.

The pulse

The blood and the tubes or vessels which carry it are the transport system of the body. You can feel the blood flowing through your body if you find your pulse. The picture on the next page shows where to find the pulse in your wrist.

The regular beating of your pulse is caused by blood spurting through an artery. If you are feeling someone else's pulse, do not use your thumb, as that has a pulse of its own. There are other pulses in your body besides the one on your wrist. They are felt where an artery passes over a bone.

If you place your hand over your heart, you can also feel a regular beat. This is not caused by blood passing through a blood vessel, but by the pumping action of the heart.

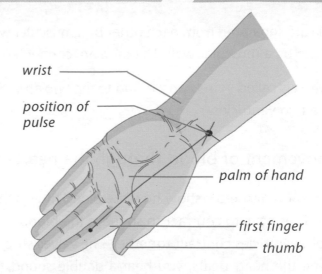

How to find the pulse in your wrist

The heart

Blood has to move round the body continuously. This is because:

- oxygen has to be taken from the lungs to the cells
- dissolved foods have to be taken from the liver to the cells
- heat generated by the liver has to be transported to the cells
- carbon dioxide and other waste chemicals have to be removed from the cells

A pump is needed to circulate the blood around the body. This is the job of the heart. The heart is a muscular pump.

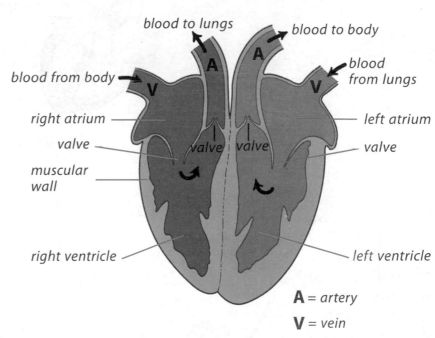

A = artery

V = vein

The heart cut downwards through the centre and viewed from the front

The heart is divided into four chambers, two at the top and two at the bottom. The top two chambers are smaller than the bottom ones, known as **atria** (singular atrium). The two bottom chambers are called **ventricles**.

The atria are separated from each other by a muscular wall. The two ventricles are also separated from each other by a muscular wall. The atria are connected to the ventricles by valves.

Blood vessels called veins carry blood to the two atria. Blood vessels called arteries carry blood away from the two ventricles.

The movement of blood through the heart

The five diagrams below show how the blood moves through the heart. The muscles of the atria and the ventricles have to contract to squeeze the blood through the heart. Both atria contract together, then both ventricles contract together. The valves stop the blood from going in the wrong direction. Each time the heart beats, you hear a double sound, 'lub dup', 'lub dup', and so on. The diagrams below will help you to understand what causes these sounds.

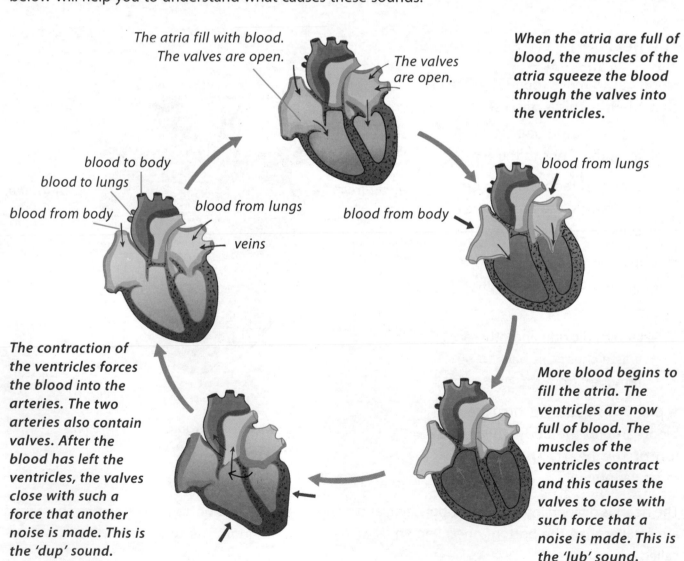

The atria fill with blood. The valves are open.

The valves are open.

When the atria are full of blood, the muscles of the atria squeeze the blood through the valves into the ventricles.

blood to body
blood to lungs
blood from body
blood from lungs
veins

blood from lungs
blood from body

The contraction of the ventricles forces the blood into the arteries. The two arteries also contain valves. After the blood has left the ventricles, the valves close with such a force that another noise is made. This is the 'dup' sound.

More blood begins to fill the atria. The ventricles are now full of blood. The muscles of the ventricles contract and this causes the valves to close with such force that a noise is made. This is the 'lub' sound.

The blood circulation

Blood in the right-hand side of the heart has returned in veins from the cells of the body. This blood contains little or no oxygen, although it has gained carbon dioxide from actively respiring cells. This deoxygenated blood must be pumped through an artery to the lungs. In the lungs, the blood absorbs more oxygen and gives up its carbon dioxide. Blood in the left-hand side of the heart contains oxygen. This blood has to be pumped along arteries to all the cells of the body. Blood passes between the right-hand side and the left-hand side of the heart via the lungs. The blood goes through the heart twice in one complete circulation of the body.

If you look again at the diagram of the heart on page 19, you will see that the walls of the left ventricle are much thicker than the walls of the right ventricle. This is because the right ventricle only has to pump the blood the short distance to the lungs. The left ventricle, however, has to pump blood all over the body. Therefore, the left ventricle has much more work to do and has to be more muscular.

If you ask many people where their heart is, they will point towards the left-hand side of their chests. In fact, the heart is more or less in the centre of the chest, but the two ventricles are tilted slightly towards the left-hand side of the chest. The part of the heart which people feel beating is the left ventricle, located slightly to the left of centre of the chest.

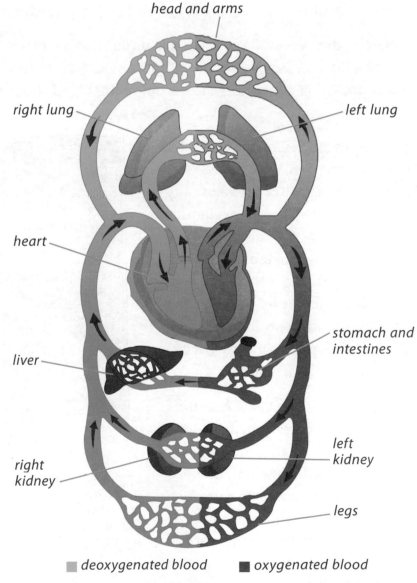

head and arms

right lung

left lung

heart

stomach and intestines

liver

left kidney

right kidney

legs

■ *deoxygenated blood*   ■ *oxygenated blood*

A simplified diagram of the circulation of blood around the body

Arteries, veins, and capillaries

When the blood leaves the heart, it is under pressure. The contraction of the ventricles pushes the blood along the arteries. Arteries always carry blood away from the heart. Because the blood is under pressure, the walls of the arteries have to be thick. When you feel your pulse, you are feeling this pressure. All of the arteries carry blood which is oxygenated (carrying oxygen), except for the pulmonary artery which carries deoxygenated blood from the heart to the lungs.

When the blood reaches the cells, it has to slow down. If it did not do so, the blood would not have time to give up food and oxygen, nor would it be able to absorb the waste chemicals produced by the cells. The blood also needs to spread out, so that it can reach every cell of the body tissues.

For these reasons, the thick-walled arteries split up into millions of tiny **blood capillaries** in the tissues. These blood capillaries have walls that are only one cell thick. This makes it easy for the dissolved food, oxygen, and other substances to pass out of the blood and for the waste products to go into the blood.

As the blood leaves the tissues, the capillaries join up again to form veins. Veins always carry blood back to the heart. All of the veins carry blood which has given up its oxygen (is deoxygenated), except for the pulmonary vein which carries oxygenated blood from the lungs to the heart. The walls of veins are not as thick or muscular as those of the arteries, as the blood is no longer under pressure. This lack of pressure means that you cannot feel a pulse in your veins.

If there is no pressure in the veins, how does the blood return to the heart, perhaps from the tips of your toes or the ends of your fingers? The answer is that the flow of blood through the veins relies upon the squeezing action of the body muscles, particularly those in the limbs, rather than the pumping action of the heart. In addition, veins have valves in them to stop the blood flowing back. The diagrams opposite show you how.

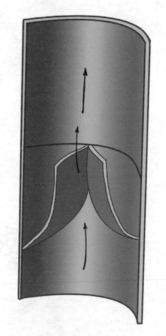 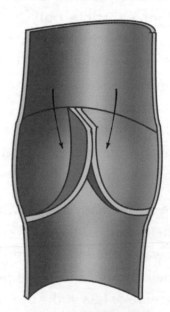

blood flowing normally to the heart in a vein. The valves are pressed flat against the walls of the vein.

blood trying to flow the wrong way in a vein. The blood collects behind the valve. This causes the valve to fall and so stop the back-flow of blood.

Valves have veins to stop the back-flow of blood

Arteries	Capillaries	Veins
Carry blood from the heart	Link arteries to veins	Carry blood to the heart
Have thick walls of muscle and elastic fibres	Walls are one cell thick.	Fairly thick walls which contain some elastic fibres
Valves present only where arteries leave the heart	No valves	Valves in the long veins of the arms and legs
Blood flows in pulses.	Blood flows steadily.	Blood flows steadily.
Blood is under high pressure.	Blood pressure changes.	Blood is under low pressure.
Blood is bright red and contains oxygen (except in the pulmonary artery).	Blood is losing oxygen and gaining carbon dioxide.	Blood is dull red and contains very little oxygen (except in the pulmonary vein).

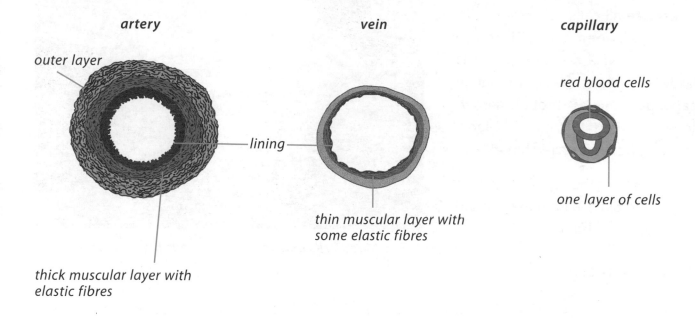

artery   *vein*   *capillary*

outer layer

lining

red blood cells

one layer of cells

thin muscular layer with some elastic fibres

thick muscular layer with elastic fibres

Comparing the three types of blood vessel

What is blood?

The body of an adult contains about 5 litres of blood and it is important to remember that blood is not just a red coloured liquid. Blood is a living tissue and just one drop of it may contain about 5 million cells. In fact, blood consists of four main parts: **red blood cells**, **white blood cells**, and **platelets**, all floating in a yellow, watery liquid called **plasma**.

Red blood cells

Most of the cells in the blood are red blood cells. Each of these is round with both surfaces hollowed out, a shape called a biconcave disc. The red colour is caused by a chemical called haemoglobin. This is a protein combined with iron and it is what lets the red blood cells carry oxygen. Red blood cells do not have a nucleus, which means they have a short life of only about 100 days. The dead cells are broken up in the liver. About 200 million red blood cells die and are replaced every day. New red blood cells are made in the bone marrow which fills the centre of the larger bones. Like all cells, red blood cells have a cell membrane, but the membrane of a red blood cell is elastic. This allows the cell to change shape, as it moves through narrow blood capillaries. In 1 mm^3 of blood, there may be 5 million red blood cells.

The main job of the red blood cells is to transport oxygen from the lungs to every cell of the body.

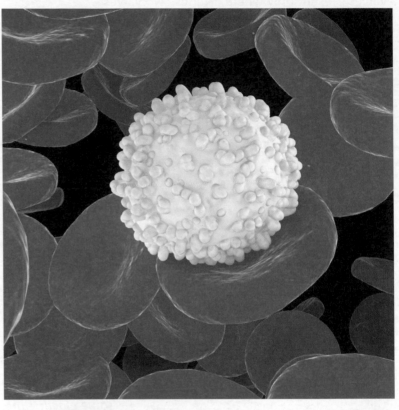

Red blood cells and white blood cells highly magnified

White blood cells

There are several types of white blood cell. Each type has a different shaped nucleus and, on average, a white blood cell is about twice as big as a red blood cell. As they have a nucleus, white blood cells can live for a long time. White blood cells are made in the bone marrow. In 1 mm^3 of blood there are about 6000 white blood cells.

White blood cells help to defend the body against disease. They are constantly on the lookout for harmful bacteria which they destroy by engulfing them (wrapping themselves round them).

Once this has happened, the white blood cells live only for a few days because they are poisoned by the bacteria they have captured. The yellow pus which comes from an infected wound is dead white blood cells that have been poisoned by the bacteria that caused the infection.

OXFORD
UNIVERSITY PRESS

Some white blood cells also produce chemicals called **antibodies**. These kill germs and change the poisonous chemicals produced by germs into harmless substances. Some antibodies remain in the blood for months or even years after they have helped you recover from a disease. While they are there, they help to stop you catching the disease again.

Platelets

Platelets are very small cell fragments made in the bone marrow. There are about 250,000 platelets in 1 mm³ of blood. Each platelet has a sticky membrane, but no nucleus. Platelets help to seal wounds by **clotting** the blood. Clotting is when the blood goes solid near the wound.

Plasma

The liquid part of the blood is called plasma. The red and white cells, and platelets float in it. Plasma is water with a large number of substances dissolved in it. These include many food chemicals, including glucose, amino acids, vitamins, and mineral salts. The plasma also carries **hormones**, the body's chemical messengers, as well as waste chemicals. It carries carbon dioxide from the body back to the lungs and another waste product, called urea, from the liver to the kidneys. Plasma also contains some blood proteins. One of these is called **fibrinogen**. Fibrinogen helps the blood to clot, so sealing up a wound. Other blood proteins include the antibodies, mentioned above, which help to protect us against germs.

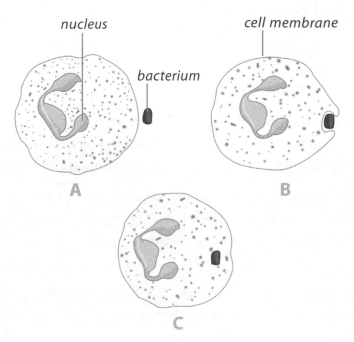

How a white blood cell engulfs a germ

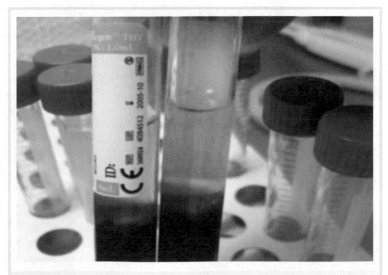

When blood is spun rapidly in a machine called a centrifuge, all the cells and platelets sink to the bottom of the tube. The pale yellow plasma can then be seen clearly.

Diseases of the transport system

Diseases of the blood circulatory system kill more people than any other disease. But the number of deaths is gradually decreasing because of modern discoveries regarding the causes, prevention, and treatment of these diseases.

Anaemia is quite common and happens when there is not enough iron in a person's diet. You may remember that iron is an important part of haemoglobin, the oxygen-carrying substance in the red blood cells. Anaemia is treated with tablets, containing iron salts.

Haemophilia is a disease that can be passed on by parents to their children. A haemophiliac cannot make the chemicals needed to make the blood clot and heal wounds. Even a small cut or scratch can bleed dangerously, unless medical treatment is given urgently.

Thrombosis is a clot or lump of blood protein and blood cells inside a blood vessel. If a thrombosis gets stuck in a blood vessel, it will stop the flow of blood. A thrombosis in the brain cuts down the blood supply to the brain. This lowers the amount of oxygen reaching the brain cells. This is what happens in a stroke, which can kill or cause brain damage.

The coronary arteries of the heart may be blocked or made narrower when fat collects in their walls. A thrombosis in these vessels stops oxygen getting to the heart muscle, so that the heart stops working properly. The person suffers great pain in the chest and the heart may stop beating. This is a heart attack or coronary thrombosis. Obese or overweight people with high blood pressure, or tobacco smokers, are more likely to have heart attacks than people of average weight. The main cause of heart disease is the build up of a fatty substance called cholesterol inside the arteries. This makes the arteries narrower and eventually clogs them up altogether. The coronary arteries supply the heart muscle with food and oxygen. If cholesterol clogs the coronary arteries, the heart may become weaker and stop beating. This is called heart failure.

Varicose veins are caused when the valves in the veins of the legs do not work properly. The veins swell and become varicose veins. In bad cases, a vein may have to be taken out of the leg. Other healthy veins are then joined up by the surgeon to carry blood up the leg.

Leaking of heart valves occurs when the valves of the heart do not shut

Varicose veins can result when the valves in the legs do not work properly.

OXFORD
UNIVERSITY PRESS

An artificial pacemaker like this is used to keep the heart beating steadily.

properly and it is unable to work efficiently. Sometimes a faulty valve can be replaced with an artificial valve. This involves opening up the heart. A heart-lung machine is used to pump the blood and breathe for the patient while the operation is carried out. The heart-lung machine does the work of both the heart and the lungs until the operation is finished.

Faulty pacemaker is a condition that occurs when the natural pacemaker of the heart stops keeping a steady pulse. The pacemaker is a group of cells in the right atrium of the heart. These produce a small pulse of electricity (about 70 times a minute). This pulse of electricity spreads through the heart muscle, making it contract. Today a person who has a faulty pacemaker can have a small artificial pacemaker that is fitted with a small battery inserted under the skin of the chest near the heart. The artificial pacemaker produces pulses of electricity which make the heart beat in rhythm.

Diabetes is a condition which occurs when enough insulin is not produced. As well as producing digestive enzymes (see page 4), the pancreas also produces the hormone insulin. This helps to control the level of glucose in the blood. Some people do not make enough insulin and glucose is not stored in their liver. Instead it is passed out of the body in the urine. People who do not produce enough insulin have to check their blood sugar level regularly. This disease is called diabetes. The person with diabetes may feel weak and sleepy, as their blood sugar level changes. Because fats and muscle proteins have to be used to supply the body with energy, the person loses weight and becomes noticeably thinner. Diabetes can be controlled by injections or tablets of insulin or by careful control of the diet.

Heart transplant is the last resort for people with heart failure where all other treatments have failed. The replacement heart is donated by someone who has been declared brain dead, often after an accident, but who remains on a life support machine. The new heart is packed in crushed ice until it is needed.

In the meantime, the heart transplant patient is connected to a heart-lung machine. This collects the blood before it reaches the heart, oxygenates it and circulates it to the rest of the body. The patient's chest is cut open and the 'new' heart is stitched in place. The blood vessels are reconnected to the heart and the 'new' heart takes over its job of pumping blood all round the body. It takes about six months for the patient to recover fully.

Unfortunately, the body's immune system can detect and destroy any foreign material in the body, treating it as if it were germs. Because of this, the body often rejects a transplanted heart. There are now drugs that reduce the risk of rejection, but the patient has to take them for the rest of his life. Transplantation lengthens the life of someone who would otherwise die and about 80 per cent of patients are alive two years after the operation and 72 per cent survive for 5 years.

1. What is the main job of the circulatory system?

2. Name four of the materials carried by the blood.

3. How much blood is there in the body of an adult human being?

4. What are the four parts of the blood? Describe what each of them does.

5. What does haemoglobin do in the body?

6. Why does lack of iron in the diet sometimes lead to anaemia?

7. A drop of blood has just left one of your lungs. Describe the route it takes to get back to the lungs.

8. Why is it much easier to stop blood flowing from a vein than an artery?

9. Why does blood spurt out of a damaged artery?

10. Why is it not correct to say that all arteries carry oxygenated blood and all veins carry deoxygenated blood?

11. Here is a simplified diagram showing a section through the human heart. In your notebook, write down the names of the parts of the diagram.

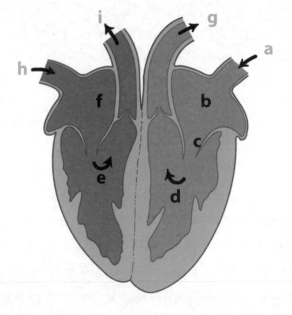

12. How do veins differ from arteries and capillaries in their structure and function?

13. What are varicose veins and what causes their development?

14. What type of people are prone to developing blood related diseases?

15. What is a pacemaker and when is it needed?

16. What work does a valve in the heart or a vein do? What is a faulty heart valve and how can it be repaired?

17. What happens if a person has high levels of glucose in his or her blood? What can be done to control the level of glucose?

18. What are the advantages and disadvantages of a heart transplant?

1. Draw an outline of the human body like this. Mark on it, with a cross, the position of each pulse that you discover.

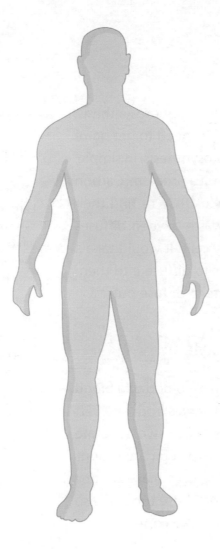

2. How many times a minute does your heart beat when you are resting? Do your heartbeats increase or decrease when you exercise? Why?

CHAPTER 4

Transport in plants

Green plants need water and carbon dioxide for photosynthesis. They need mineral salts from the soil. They need to get rid of the waste oxygen produced during photosynthesis. In simple, single-celled algae, like chlorella, this is not a problem. Carbon dioxide, water, and mineral salts simply **diffuse** or find their way in, from the surroundings, while waste oxygen diffuses out. Larger plants are made up of many cells. It would take a long time for gases and other materials to diffuse into them from the outside and for waste products to diffuse out.

The importance of phloem and xylem

Plants do not have a heart, nor do they have blood or a blood system, but they do need to transport materials from one part of the plant to another. To do this they have two separate transport systems. These are based on two separate groups of cells called **xylem** and **phloem**. These cells make up tiny tubes running the full length of the plant. These tubes are so small that they can only be seen with a microscope.

xylem

phloem

A vertical section of a plant stem seen through a microscope

BASIC FACTS

- Simple, single-celled, plant-like organisms move materials in and out of their bodies by diffusion.
- Larger plants have two transport systems, one based on xylem vessels, which moves water and mineral salts, the other based on phloem tissue which moves food substances.
- Water enters the root hairs of a plant by a process called osmosis.
- Mineral salts enter the roots by the processes of diffusion and active transport.
- Gases enter and leave the aerial parts of a plant by diffusion through the stomata or lenticels.
- The movement of oxygen and carbon dioxide through a plant takes place by diffusion through the air spaces between the cells.
- Transpiration is the evaporation of water from the leaves of a plant.
- Transpiration from the leaves causes water to be pulled up the stem in the xylem vessels; this is the transpiration stream.
- The rate of transpiration increases in bright sunlight and in warm, dry, and moving air.
- Food is moved to where it is needed by the phloem in the veins of leaves, roots, and stems.
- The transport of food and mineral salts in plants is called translocation.

Xylem moves water and dissolved mineral salts from the roots to the leaves. Phloem moves food substances from the leaves, where they were made, to the rest of the plant. The xylem and phloem do not transport oxygen and carbon dioxide. These gases move into the plant by diffusion. Plants do not need rapid supplies of oxygen and food, because they are never active in the way that animals are.

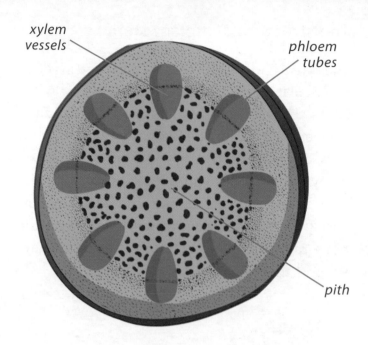

xylem vessels

phloem tubes

pith

A cross-section of a plant stem

Xylem consists of long, empty, dead cells, which form tiny tubes called vessels. Phloem consists of living cells arranged end to end. Unlike xylem vessels, the cross-walls of phloem tubes do not disappear. Instead, they develop perforations like a sieve. These cross walls are called sieve plates, while the tubes are called sieve tubes. It is through the sieve tubes that the foods, such as sugars, are transported. Phloem tissue also contains companion cells, so-called because they grow by the side of the sieve tubes. The companion cells are believed to be essential for the movement of foods through the sieve tubes of the phloem.

Water and mineral salts travel in the xylem, up the plant stem, from the roots to the leaves nearly all the time. At the same time, the phloem carries the food made in the leaves, down to the roots to be stored, as in carrots, to underground stems, as in potatoes, or up the stem to the growing buds, flowers, or developing fruits.

Tissue	Name of process	Substances moved	Structure
Xylem	Transpiration	Water and mineral salts moved from the roots to the leaves	Columns of hollow, dead, reinforced cells
Phloem	Translocation	Moves food substances from the leaves to the rest of the plant	Columns of living cells

The structure of a plant stem

The xylem and phloem cells are arranged in veins, or vascular bundles, in the stem and leaves. In the stem, the vascular bundles are arranged in a circular pattern, just beneath the outer layer of cells, or epidermis. The vascular bundles contain many strong fibres and this helps to make the stem strong and able to withstand being bent by strong winds. The xylem vessels themselves also have reinforced cell walls and these help to support the weight of the plant.

The structure of the plant root

The plant roots have to be able to resist the pulling or stretching force, when the stem above is blown about by the wind. In the root, the xylem and phloem of the vascular bundle are in the centre, so as to resist these forces. Xylem carries water and mineral salts from the root to the stem. Phloem brings food from the stem to the root, providing the root cells with all the food substances they need for their energy and growth.

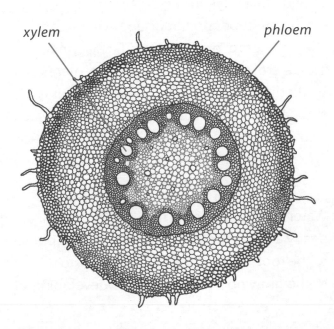

A section through a plant root. The xylem and the phloem are in the centre of the root to withstand the stretching forces when the stem is being blown about in the wind.

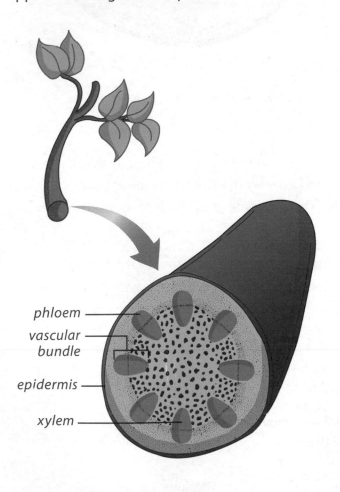

In a stem, the vascular bundles are arranged near the edge of the stem, to help give the stem strength and to help it resist the bending forces of the wind.

OXFORD
UNIVERSITY PRESS

Water enters the plant

At the very tip of a root are several layers of cells which form the **root cap**. These cells are replaced as fast as they are worn away as the root tip pushes its way through the soil. Just behind the root cap are thousands of tiny, tube-like growths, called **root hairs**

In the soil, the root hairs grow between the soil particles. The root hairs take up water from the soil. This process is called **osmosis**. The water in the soil is, in fact, a very weak solution of mineral salts. Inside each of the root hair cells, there is a concentrated solution of sugars, mineral salts, and other substances. This solution makes up what is called the cell sap. The cell membrane around each plant cell has a special structure with many tiny holes in it. These holes are big enough to let water molecules through, though the larger molecules of mineral salts are unable to pass. A membrane such as this, which will let some molecules through, but not others, is called a **semi-permeable membrane**.

If you think of one root hair growing between soil particles, its cell sap is a stronger solution than that of the soil water. Water from the soil goes through the cell membrane and into the cell sap by osmosis, until the cell sap and the soil water are at the same concentration. The mineral salts in the soil solution are left behind. The cell sap of our root hair now has a lower concentration than that of the cell next to it. Water, therefore, passes from this root hair to the neighbouring cell, until both have cell sap of the same concentration. This continues until the water has reached the xylem vessels.

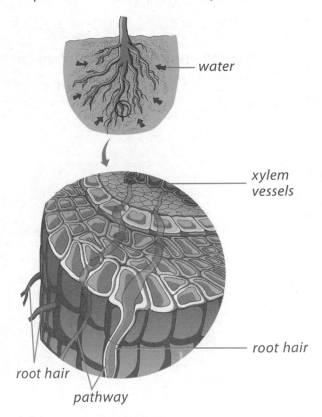

water

xylem vessels

root hair

root hair

pathway

How water enters a plant root by osmosis

Mineral salts enter the roots

Some mineral salts enter the root hairs by **diffusion** and are eventually carried up the xylem vessels. Diffusion is the spreading out of a substance from an area of high concentration to an area of low concentration. If you put a drop of ink in a bowl of water, without shaking or stirring the water, the ink will spread out or diffuse through the water. Eventually, the bowl will contain a uniformly pale blue (or pale black) mixture. If you put a drop of ink into a swimming pool after a very long time, the same thing will happen. Like osmosis, diffusion does not need energy. Some of the mineral salts in the soil enter the plant roots by this process of diffusion.

Other mineral salts enter the roots by what is called **active transport**. If diffusion were the only method by which a cell could take in substances, it would have no control over what went into or out of it. Anything that was more concentrated outside could diffuse into the cell, whether it was harmful or not. Scientists do not fully understand the process of active transport, but it seems certain that the cell has to use energy (from respiration) to move mineral salts from the soil (where they are in low concentration) across the cell membrane. The special proteins called **enzymes** are also involved in active transport.

As a result of the processes of osmosis and diffusion, the water and dissolved mineral salts in the roots move from cell to cell, until they reach the xylem. The water and dissolved mineral salts then travel up the xylem vessels of the roots, stems, and leaf veins.

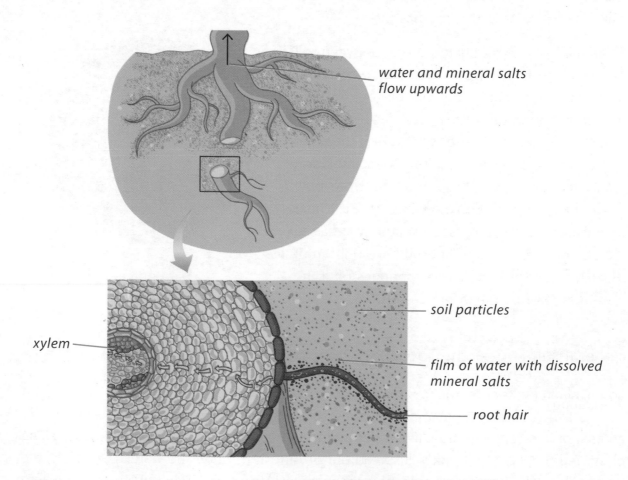

water and mineral salts flow upwards

soil particles

xylem

film of water with dissolved mineral salts

root hair

How water and mineral salts move from the soil into the root of a plant

OXFORD
UNIVERSITY PRESS

Transpiration

Water and dissolved mineral salts from the roots move very quickly through the xylem and up the stem and leaves. The main force which draws water up the plant is caused by a process called **transpiration**. Water evaporates from the leaves and diffuses out of the tiny pores, the **stomata**, on the undersides of the leaves. As the water is evaporated, more is drawn out of the xylem to replace it. As the xylem cells form a series of continuous tubes from the leaves, down the stem to the roots, there is a flow of water and dissolved mineral salts from the roots to the leaves. This flow is called the **transpiration stream**.

The speed of transpiration varies with the condition of the plant and its surroundings. When water is in short supply, or if the roots of the plants are damaged, the plant slows down the rate of transpiration by **wilting**. But there are other things which affect the transpiration rate, as shown in table on page 36.

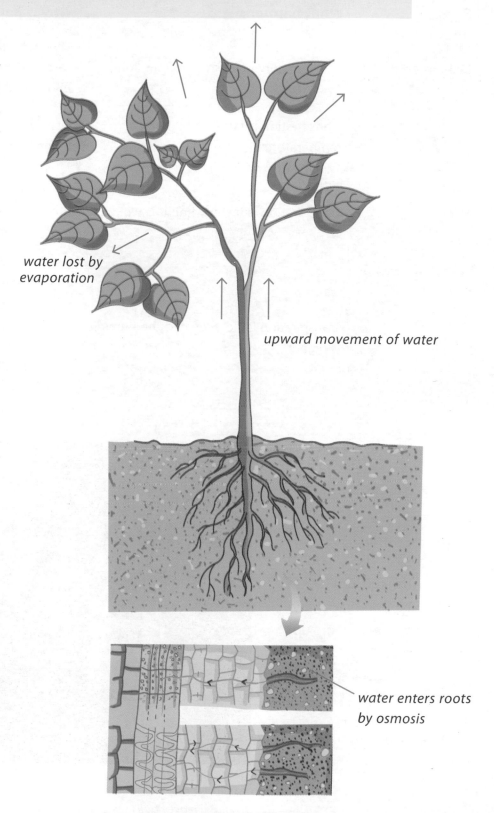

water lost by evaporation

upward movement of water

water enters roots by osmosis

The transpiration stream

Factor	What happens	Why it happens
Light intensity	Transpiration increases in bright light.	The stomata open wider to allow more carbon dioxide into the leaf for photosynthesis.
Temperature	Transpiration is faster in higher temperatures.	Evaporation and diffusion are faster at higher temperatures.
Wind	Transpiration is faster when it is windy.	Air movement removes water vapour quickly, speeding up the diffusion of more water vapour out of the leaf.
Humidity	Transpiration is slower when the humidity is higher.	Evaporation and diffusion of water vapour out of the leaf slows down if the leaf is already surrounded by moist air. In dry air, the diffusion of water vapour from the leaf to the atmosphere will be rapid.

On a large tree, there may be countless thousands of leaves from which water is evaporating. As a result, water is pulled up the xylem vessels with a tremendous force. The force is big enough to draw water 50 metres or more up the trunks of big trees. Added to this, water is also pushed up the stem or trunk by a pressure acting on it from the roots. This pressure is called the **root pressure**

Some of these Californian redwood trees are over 100 metres tall. Transpiration from the leaves pulls water up their trunks.

OXFORD
UNIVERSITY PRESS

The transport of food

The food made in the leaves by photosynthesis is carried away in the sieve tubes of the phloem. The food may travel up or down the stem, according to which parts of the plant need it at the time. Food is mainly carried in the form of sugar sucrose, but scientists do not fully understand how it is moved. We do know that the movement of food depends on living processes in the phloem cells and anything which harms the living cells of the phloem also stops the transport of food materials. The transport of food and mineral salts in plants is sometimes called **translocation**

The transport of gases

If you are sitting in a room and someone comes in wearing perfume and sits at the other end, the smell of the perfume quickly fills the whole room. The molecules of the perfume, a vapour, move about freely until they have spread out, or diffused, evenly across the whole room.

This same process of diffusion is how gases move in and out of a plant. During respiration, oxygen is taken in and carbon dioxide is given out. In the daylight, when photosynthesis is faster than respiration, carbon dioxide diffuses in, while oxygen diffuses out. In the leaves and green stems of plants, the gases enter and leave through the stomata. Then they diffuse between the air spaces between the cells to reach all parts of the stem or leaf. There are no stomata in the woody stems of plants. Instead, gases have to pass through small openings in the bark called **lenticels**

Roots obtain their oxygen from the air spaces between the soil particles. Most of this oxygen is dissolved in the soil water, which enters the root through the growing region and the root hairs.

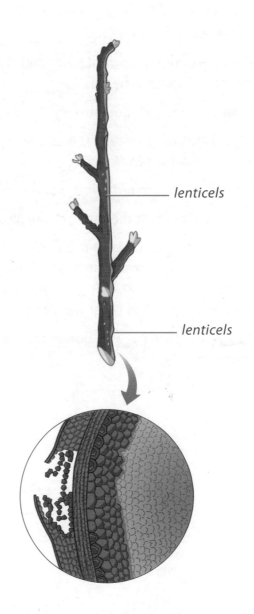

lenticels

lenticels

Lenticels on the bark of a young tree

1. Why do larger, multicellular (many-celled) plants need a transport system?

2. What are the names of the two sets of tubes which make up the transport system of a plant?

3. Whereabouts would you find the two sets of transport tubes in a leaf?

4. What is the name of the process by which water enters the root hairs?

5. Which set of tubes carries water and dissolved mineral salts?
Describe how it does it.

6. Which set of tubes carry dissolved food to storage areas, growing points, and other places where it is needed?

7. Most garden plants would wilt and die if you watered them with a strong salt solution. Explain why this is.

8. What is a transpiration stream?

9. What kinds of climate and weather conditions do you think will produce a high rate of transpiration? Explain your answer.

10. Explain why a potted plant placed on a sunny windowsill will soon start to wilt.

11. Why do you think the rate of transpiration is greatly reduced at night?

12. A leafy plant shoot, plus the beaker of water in which it was placed, weighed 305 grams. Two hours later, it weighed 280 grams. An identical beaker of water, without a plant, lost 4 grams over the same length of time. What was the rate of transpiration of the plant per hour?

13. Why in the summer is it better to water potted plants during the evening than during the day?

Things to do

1. If you were given a potted plant, how would you show that it loses water by transpiration? Draw a labelled diagram, showing what you would do. Explain any precautions you would take to show that the water had actually come from the plant.

2. Devise an experiment to compare the effects of two different chemical fertilizers on a species of flowering plant. What equipment and materials would you use? What measurements would you make? How would you make sure that your comparison was fair?

3. Get two potted plants that are roughly the same size. One should be a plant with leaves such as a busy lizzie or pelargonium. The other should be a cactus or some other succulent plant. Water the plants thoroughly and put them on a windowsill. Look at them every day, but do not water them. Keep a record of any changes you see.

Reproduction in plants

CHAPTER 5

BASIC FACTS

- The flower contains the plant's reproductive organs.

- There are four main parts to most flowers: sepals, petals, stamens, and carpels.

- The sepals are green and leaf-like. They protect the flower in the bud.

- The petals, when present, are brightly coloured to attract insects.

- The stamens are the male parts of the flower. They each consist of a filament and an anther which contains the pollen grains.

- The carpels are the female parts of the flower. They consist of stigma, style, and ovary.

- Pollination is the transfer of pollen from a stamen to a carpel.

- During self-pollination, pollen is transferred from a stamen to a stigma on the same plant.

- During cross-pollination, pollen is transferred from the stamen of one flower to the stigma of a flower on another plant.

- Insect-pollinated plants have brightly coloured petals, scented flowers with nectaries, sticky stigmas, and pollen grains which are large and sticky.

- Wind-pollinated plants usually have dull green flowers, often without petals, they have no scent or nectaries. The stamens have long filaments, so a lot of pollen is blown away, while the stigmas are feathery to catch the pollen as it blows past. When a pollen grain lands on a stigma, a pollen tube grows down the style to the ovary.

- A nucleus from the male sex cell then moves down to join with a female sex cell (an ovule) in the ovary.

- Fertilization is when the two nuclei join.

- The fertilized ovule forms a seed and the ovary forms a fruit. Plants use animals, the wind, water, and explosive methods to disperse or scatter their seeds.

- Each seed contains a dormant or resting embryo plant.

- Germination is when seeds start to grow.

- A seed will often lie dormant or resting until the conditions are right for it to grow.

- The three things that must be just right for a seed to start germinating are temperature, air conditions (oxygen), and enough water.

- Some plants can reproduce asexually. Asexual reproduction in plants is also called vegetative reproduction or vegetative propagation.

- In vegetative reproduction, the new plant is an exact copy of its parent. In sexual reproduction, the new plant may be different from its parents.

- Some of the ways in which plants reproduce asexually or vegetatively include runners, tubers, rooting branches, bulbs, and corms. Some plants can also be reproduced vegetatively by the method called stem cuttings.

Reproduction

Nothing lives forever. And yet, life continues because all living things are able to produce copies of themselves. If living things did not reproduce themselves, then before long there would be none left. As each plant or animal grew older and finally died, it would not be replaced. Eventually, all the different kinds of plants and animals would die out. They would become extinct.

Only those kind of plant or animal, or species, survive that reproduce. A house mouse, dragonfly, fox, frog, buttercup, or daisy plant may live for only a few weeks or a few years. But as long as some members of each species reproduce and some of their young grow up and also reproduce, then the species will continue to survive on Earth.

Plant sexual reproduction

Most plants, including trees, reproduce by means of seeds. Seeds are made because of what is called **sexual reproduction**. In sexual reproduction, a tiny male cell joins with an egg or female cell. This joining of male and female cells is called **fertilization**. In plants it can also produce seeds. It is the flower which contains the reproductive organs and fertilization takes place in the flower.

The parts of a flower

Some flowers contain only the male sex organs, while others have only female sex organs. But most flowers, like the one in the picture below, contain both male and female sex organs. There are four parts to such flowers. These are the **sepals**, the **petals**, the **stamens**, and the **carpels**. They are arranged in rings, one inside the other.

The sepals protect the flower when it is in bud. They are usually green and leaf-like.

The petals are often brightly coloured and scented. There may be a nectary at the base of each petal which produces a sugary nectar.

The stamens are the male reproductive organs. Each consists of an anther which contains pollen grains and a stalk called the filament. Pollen grains contain the male sex cells.

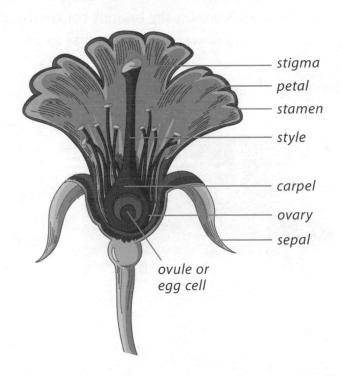

The parts of a typical flower

stigma
petal
stamen
style
carpel
ovary
sepal
ovule or egg cell

The carpels are the female reproductive organs. Each carpel contains one or more ovaries in which the tiny ovules or egg-cells are found. An ovule contains the female sex cell and each ovule can grow into a seed. Above the ovary is a narrow stalk called the style and this ends in the stigma. The stigma is often sticky, so that pollen grains can stick to it.

Pollination

A flower must be **pollinated** before it can make seeds. This means it must receive the pollen from another flower of the same species before fertilization can take place. **Self-pollination** is the transfer of pollen from a stamen to the stigma of the same flower or, to another flower on the same plant. **Cross-pollination** is the transfer of pollen between the stamens of one flower to the stigma of a flower on a different plant of the same species. There are several ways in which this can happen. Cross-pollination gives a wider variety of young plants than self-pollination. This helps the plant species to survive if the conditions where it is growing, change. Self-pollination produces young plants which are almost the same as the parent plant. To prevent self-pollination, flowers often have stamens and carpels which ripen at different times.

The pollen of plants is mainly carried by insects, such as bees and butterflies, or by the wind. A few flowers are pollinated by birds, bats, or other animals. Flowers which have pollen carried by insects are usually brightly coloured and have nectar or a sweet smell. As they go from flower to flower, the insects may spread the pollen.

Insect-pollinated flowers

The open, cup-shape of the geranium flower allows many small insects to visit it and pollinate it.

Insect-pollinated flowers include those of roses, petunias, morning glory, lupins, pears, pomegranates, plums, cherries, and many others. Insects do not carry pollen from flower to flower for free. They are rewarded for their services because they can eat some of the pollen and as many insect-pollinated flowers produce nectar, the insects can feed on that too.

The geranium flower can be pollinated by a variety of insects which walk around inside the flower, in search of the nectar at the base of the petals. The stamens ripen before the carpels, so that an insect visiting a young geranium flower will be dusted with pollen. When this insect next visits an older flower, the carpels will be ripe and their stigmas will pick up the pollen from the insect's body.

OXFORD
UNIVERSITY PRESS

Some flowers are constructed so that when an insect lands on one of them, the weight of the insect's body makes the stamens jerk down, covering the insect's back with pollen.

One interesting case is that of a bee orchid, whose flower looks like a female bumble bee. When a male bumble bee sees the flower, he tries to mate with it and gets covered with pollen. When he tries the same thing with another bee orchid, he pollinates it.

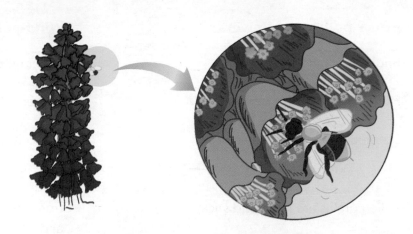

The anthers and stigmas of the insect-pollinated flowers of lupin ripen at different times.

The flowers of a bee orchid resemble a female bumble bee.

Wind-pollinated flowers

Flowers, such as those of grasses and many large trees, do not have brightly coloured petals or nectar. These flowers are pollinated by the wind. The pollen of wind-pollinated flowers is very light and it blows easily. Why do you think it is that most wind-pollinated flowers do not have petals?

Many trees, like this hazel, have flowers which lack petals because they are pollinated by the wind.

Insect-pollinated flowers	Wind-pollinated flowers
Brightly-coloured petals	Either no petals or small dull petals
Flower tends to face upwards	Flowers hang down for easy shaking by the wind
Scented flowers with nectaries	No scent or nectaries
Pollen grains are large and sticky	Produce vast quantities of lightweight pollen grains from anthers which are on long filaments or stalks and which hang outside the flower.
Stigma like a sticky pinhead, to take the pollen off the insect's body, as it goes from plant to plant to feed in the nectaries	Spreading feathery stigmas to catch the passing pollen grains.

Pollination by birds

Hummingbirds, sunbirds, honeyeaters, honey creepers, and spiderhunters are the most common bird pollinators. These birds are mostly found in North, Central, and South America. Flowers pollinated by birds are often tube-shaped and usually bright red, orange, or yellow in colour. The flowers have very little scent, but they do produce large amounts of nectar. The pollen grains produced by bird-pollinated flowers are large and sticky so that they stick to the feathers of the bird.

Some species of hummingbird pollinate flowers.

OXFORD
UNIVERSITY PRESS

Pollination by bats

Most of the bat species that pollinate flowers are found in Africa, South-East Asia, the southern United States, Central America, and the Pacific Islands. Many fruits are dependent on their flowers being pollinated by bats, including mangoes, bananas, and guavas, as well as the baobab and kapok trees, and some cacti. The bats that pollinate flowers are mostly flying foxes and fruit bats. Bat-pollinated flowers are often large and bell-shaped, white or pale-coloured, and they open their petals at night. The flowers usually produce large amounts of nectar and give off a smell that attracts the bats. The pollen sticks to the fur on the bats' faces and bodies. As well as feeding on the pollen, nectar, and other parts of the flower, the bats often find insects to eat inside the flowers.

Fertilization

Fertilization occurs after pollination. Some of the pollen grains carried by the wind, insects, birds, or bats may reach a carpel and stick to the ripe stigma. Each pollen grain produces a tiny tube which grows down the style, into the ovary and towards the ovules or egg-cells. When one of the tubes reaches an ovule, it bursts open. A male nucleus from the pollen grain then moves down the **pollen tube** to join with the nucleus of the female sex cell, the ovule. When the nuclei of the pollen grains and ovules have joined together, the ovules are said to be **fertilized**.

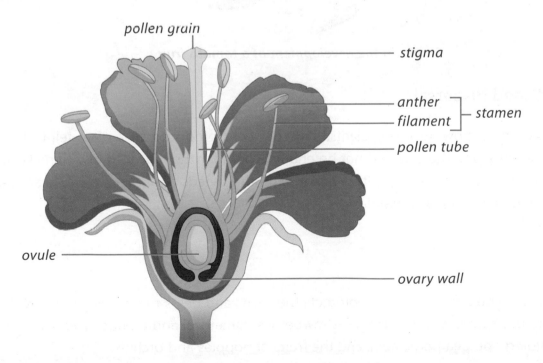

How fertilization occurs in a flowering plant

The fertilized ovule then divides up into a ball of cells, which eventually becomes a miniature plant, called the embryo. This remains in the centre of the ovule and becomes surrounded by a special tissue called endosperm. When the embryo later begins to grow, the endosperm supplies it with food. Meanwhile, the ovule itself becomes the seed and its outer wall hardens to form the tough seed coat. While this is happening, the ovary develops into a fruit.

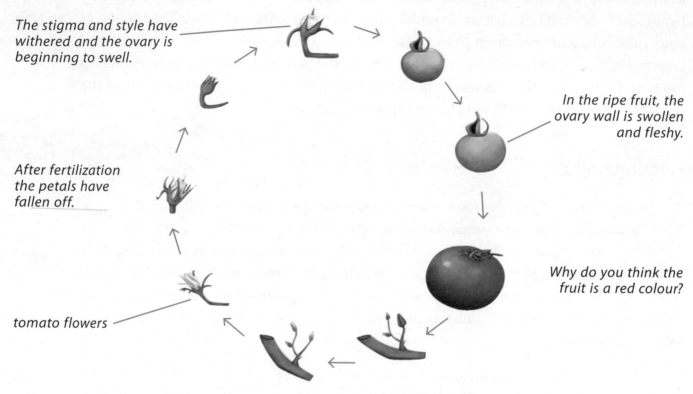

The stigma and style have withered and the ovary is beginning to swell.

In the ripe fruit, the ovary wall is swollen and fleshy.

After fertilization the petals have fallen off.

Why do you think the fruit is a red colour?

tomato flowers

Stages in the development of a tomato fruit

Seeds and seed dispersal

Seeds need room to grow into new plants. If all the seeds produced by a plant fell to the ground around the parent plant, there would not be enough room for them all to grow. To make sure they can grow without too much competition from each other, seeds are dispersed or scattered as far away from the parent plant as possible.

Fruits

Most seeds are inside a fruit. The fruit protects the seeds and helps to disperse them. Not all fruits are fleshy like the apples, pears, bananas, strawberries, tomatoes, and oranges you eat. Many fruits are dry, including ripe pea pods, nuts, and the fruits of poppies and orchids.

Animal dispersal

Brightly coloured and juicy fruits, such as blackberries, strawberries, raspberries, and gooseberries, are often eaten by animals, especially birds. The hard seeds inside these fruits pass out of the animal's body in its droppings. The seeds may end up a long way from where they were first eaten. Squirrels and jays may bury acorns and nuts, ready to eat later in the winter. These animals often forget where they have hidden their fruits and so, some grow the following spring.

cherry   strawberry

Fruits dispersed by animals

A number of seeds and fruits, such as those of goosegrass, burdock, and wood avens, have hooks that catch on the fur or feathers of animals, or even on people's clothes. If the seeds eventually drop on the soil, they may grow.

Wind, water, and 'explosive' dispersal

Many seeds are carried by the wind. The seeds of sycamore, ash, maple, and pine trees have wings, while dandelion and thistle seeds have hairy parachutes on them. Poppy and orchid fruits have small holes in them. When the wind rocks the plant, the seeds are scattered as if from a pepper pot.

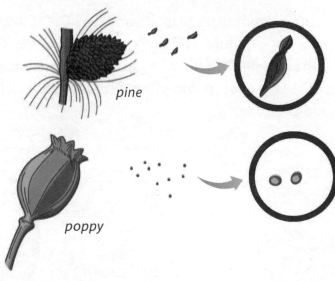

pine

poppy

Wind dispersal

thistle

The fruits of peas, lupins, laburnum, and gorse are pods. When these dry the pods split open, curl back, and suddenly shoot the seeds away from the parent plant.

The pod splits and twists open, scattering the seeds by an 'explosive' mechanism.

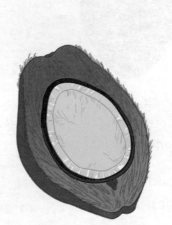

A few seeds are dispersed by water. The best-known is the coconut, which has a spongy layer of fibres around it. The fibres trap air so the coconut can float, sometimes for hundreds of kilometres, from one island to another. The seeds of water lilies and alder trees have a smaller spongy covering which lets them float in lakes and rivers.

Germination

Inside every seed is a miniature plant or **embryo**. The embryo consists of a miniature root or **radicle** a miniature shoot or **plumule**, and one or two seed leaves or **cotyledons**. There is also a food store put there by the parent plant. In some species, this is contained in the cotyledons. In others, it is a mass of cells called the endosperm, which surrounds the embryo. Around the embryo and endosperm is a tough seed coat.

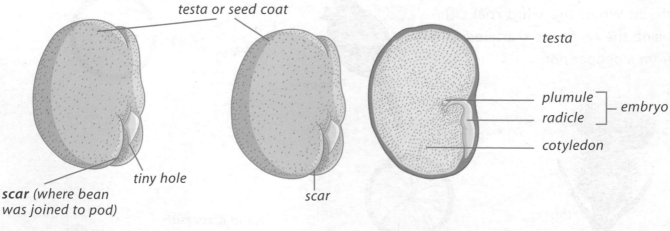

A broad bean seed

Inside a broad bean seed

The embryo remains **dormant** or resting, until the conditions are right for it to start to grow. Some seeds can stay dormant in the soil for up to 50 years. But seeds 3000 years old, from an archaeological site have been made to germinate.

All seeds need water, air, and warmth before they will start to grow. When a seed does have water, warmth, and air, it can begin to grow into a new plant. This is called **germination**

When a seed, such as a broad bean or French bean is sown, the seed first takes in water which makes it swell. There is a tiny hole in the side of the seed which is where the pollen tube entered the ovule. It is through this hole that the seed takes up water. The embryo starts to grow and its tiny radicle or root pushes through the seed coat to the outside. As the root grows downwards, tiny hairs grow out of it into the soil. These root hairs take in water and dissolved mineral salts from the soil.

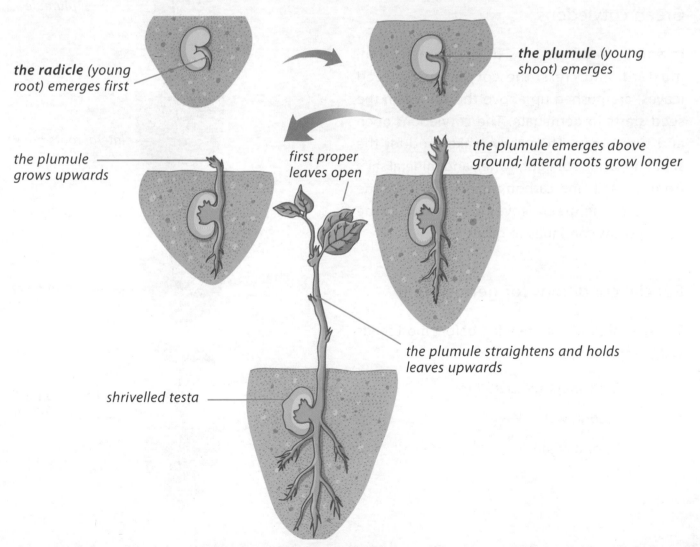

the radicle (young root) emerges first

the plumule (young shoot) emerges

the plumule grows upwards

first proper leaves open

the plumule emerges above ground; lateral roots grow longer

the plumule straightens and holds leaves upwards

shrivelled testa

The germination of a broad bean seed

Next, a young shoot begins to grow up towards the light. Soon, when it is above the ground, the shoot grows green leaves. Until this time, the seedling has not been able to make any food for itself. It has been fed by two thick seed leaves or **cotyledons**, which occupy most of the inside of the seed. These cotyledons are packed with food, put there by the parent plant. After a time, new leaves and roots are formed and we now have a small plant or seedling. There is a little bud at the top of the small plant, which will go on growing.

Green cotyledons

In some seeds, such as dwarf French bean, mustard, and cress, the cotyledons or seed leaves, are pushed up above the soil when the seed starts to germinate. The cotyledons open and turn green. Then they make food for the seedling, using sunlight, water, and mineral salts from the soil, and carbon dioxide gas from the air. Later, true green leaves are formed as the young plant continues to grow.

Special conditions for germination

The special conditions needed before most seeds will germinate are:

- The correct temperature
- Enough water
- Air or oxygen

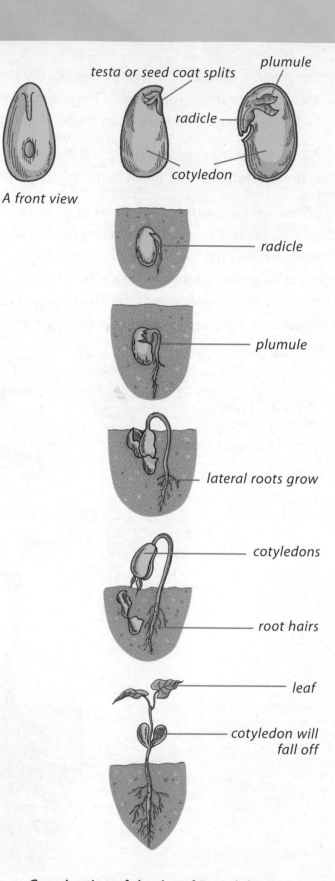

A front view

Germination of the dwarf French bean

OXFORD
UNIVERSITY PRESS

However, a few plants have seeds which need special conditions. Some tree seeds will not germinate before they have been dormant in very cold conditions (like those of winter), followed by warmer temperatures, like those which occur in the spring. Most seeds are not affected by light or darkness, but some seeds of forest plants need light before they will germinate. They will not grow until a tree or branch falls, allowing light to reach the forest floor. Many native Australian plant seeds will not germinate unless they have been scorched by a fire, while some seeds will only germinate after they have been through the digestive system of an animal. The animal's digestive juices have to weaken the seed coat enough to allow the seedling inside to emerge.

Asexual reproduction

Although all flowering plants reproduce sexually—that is why they have flowers—some can also reproduce **asexually**. Asexual reproduction in plants is also called **vegetative reproduction** or **vegetative propagation**

Sexual reproduction allows the formation of new varieties of plants because it combines features of both the male parent and the female parent plant. Asexual reproduction produces plants that are exactly like the parent plant which produced it. The new plant is produced from one parent plant's body. This can be a big advantage if, say, we have used sexual reproduction to breed a new variety of plant that has features we particularly want to keep. If we have bred a strawberry plant that has large, sweet fruits without the pips and we produce new plants from it, using asexual reproduction, the new plants will all have the large, sweet fruits without pips.

There are many different kinds of asexual reproduction in plants. They include:

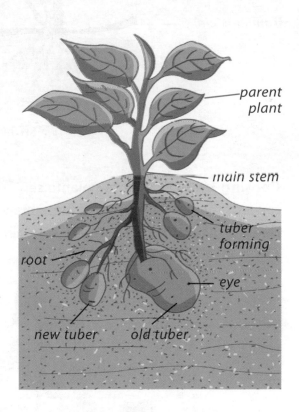

Potato tubers

Tubers: Potato plants have flowers and seeds, but we do not usually grow potatoes from seeds. Instead we plant potato **tubers**. A tuber is the part of the potato we eat and it is an underground stem that is swollen with food. Every potato has several 'eyes' on it. These are buds which, when a potato is planted, grow and send out shoots and roots to form new plants. The shoots and roots are able to grow quickly because they use the food stored in the tuber. Some of the underground stems on the new plants will become swollen with stored food and eventually form new tubers.

Runners: A strawberry plant will produce flowers and seeds, but during the growing season, it will also send out stems that grow just above the surface of the soil. Buds form at intervals along these 'runners' and new strawberry plants grow from the buds.

parent plant

new plant

runner (stem)

new plant growing from bud

Strawberry runners

Rooting branch: Bramble plants send out long, woody branches which eventually droop down towards the soil. When one of these branches touches the soil, the swollen bud at the end of it sends down roots and shoots, which eventually form a new bramble plant.

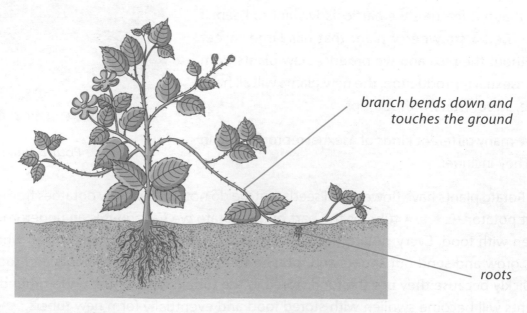

branch bends down and touches the ground

roots

The rooting branch of a bramble plant

Bulbs and corms: If you have ever cut an onion in half, you will know that it is made up of closely-packed layers. These are leaves that are packed with stored food. The onion is really a swollen bud. A daffodil, tulip, or hyacinth bulb is built in the same way. At the centre of the bulb is a bud, and if the bulb is planted, this bud will grow and produce a new plant. During the summer, new bulbs will form at the side of the parent one. If these bulbs are put in moist, warm soil, they will eventually form new plants. A corm, from which a crocus plant grows, is the swollen base of a stem, and from that new corms are eventually formed.

Cuttings: In some plants, when a branch or short stem is cut off and placed in soil, roots will grow from the cut stem and eventually form a new plant. With a few plants, such as mint, Pelargoniums, or Coleus, it is not even necessary to plant the cutting in soil. Standing it in water is often all that is required for the cutting to form a new plant.

Crocus corm

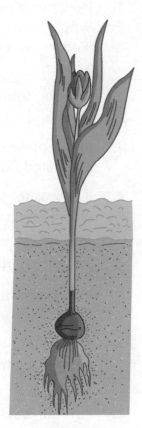

Tulip bulb

Cutting of Coleus

Cutting of Pelargonium

Questions

1. How many plants do you know of that may be in danger of becoming extinct? Why are they in danger? What is being done to save them? Write an account called 'Endangered Plants', describing plant species which are in danger of becoming extinct.

2. Working from the outside in, list the parts of a flower. Make a sketch of each of the parts and say what its job or function is.

3. Insect-pollinated flowers produce fewer and larger pollen grains than wind-pollinated flowers. Explain why this is so.

4. If you were growing plants, such as cucumber or melon plants, in a greenhouse where insects could not enter, how would you make sure that all the flowers were pollinated?

5. What is the difference between pollination and fertilization in plants?

6. How does the nucleus in a pollen grain get from the stigma to the ovary of a flower?

7. Think about the meaning of these words: fruit, seed, germinate, cotyledons, embryo, plumule, dormancy, root hairs. Write a sentence containing each of these words.

8. List four ways in which plants disperse or scatter their seeds.

9. Why do you think that seeds formed in the autumn do not grow until the following spring? And why will seeds formed in dry weather not start to grow until there is rain?

10. Which parts of a tomato flower

    i. grow to form the fruit,

    ii. fall off after fertilization,

    iii. remain joined to the fruit?

11. Gardeners sometimes cut a large potato tuber in half before they plant it in order to obtain more plants. Where should they make the cut?

12. What are the advantages of vegetative reproduction over sexual reproduction in plants? What are the disadvantages?

OXFORD
UNIVERSITY PRESS

Things to do

1. Look at some flowers with a hand lens. Can you see the different parts of the flowers? Do all flowers have the same number of sepals, petals, stamens, and carpels? Make a list of the flowers you have inspected and number the various parts of each.

2. Look at the flowers in the garden or collect pictures of garden and wild flowers from magazines and seed catalogues. Record the name and colour of each flower. Make a histogram or bar chart of flower colours. What are the most common flower colours? Which coloured flowers are least common?

3. Make a graph to show when wild flowers can be found flowering. Obtain a large sheet of squared paper and draw in two thick lines as axes. Write in the months of the year along the horizontal axis. As you see or read about a wild flower, fill in the square or squares when it can be seen flowering.

4. The words 'annuals', 'perennials', and biennials' are sometimes used in connection with garden flowers. Find out what these words mean. Make a table of garden flowers showing which are annuals, biennials, and perennials. Look at a seed catalogue to help you with this.

5. What happens if seeds are planted too close together? Plan an investigation using, say, marigold or nasturtium seeds to test your ideas. What will you plant the seeds in? How will you look after all the seeds in the same way to make sure your test is fair? What measurements or records will you collect?

Environment and feeding relationships

BASIC FACTS

- The environment is the surroundings of a living thing.
- A habitat is the natural home of an organism where it lives and reproduces.
- Animals and plants are adapted to living in their particular habitat.
- Living things in a habitat depend upon one another for food, shelter, and protection.
- A habitat can change from day to day, from season to season, or over a much longer period of time.
- An ecosystem is all the living things and their physical environment, including air, water, temperature, and soil conditions in a particular place.
- Green plants are the starting point for food chains and food webs.
- Green plants are the producers, animals are the consumers, and many bacteria and fungi are decomposers.
- A food chain not only shows how one organism feeds on another, it also shows how energy moves along the chain. The reason that most food chains have only four or five links is because at each stage energy is lost to the surroundings, mainly as heat. Only a small amount of energy is stored for growth. This stored energy is then passed to the next consumer in the food chain.
- Pyramids of numbers show the decrease in the number of organisms from one link to another along a food chain.
- Pyramids of biomass show the decrease in the mass of organisms from one link to another along a food chain.
- In an ecosystem, several food chains are interconnected to form a food web.
- Even a small change in a food chain or food web, is likely to affect all the plants and animals in the food chain or food web.
- A succession is a gradual change in the plant and animal species living in an area.

Habitats

A habitat is any place where a group of organisms can live. Ponds, streams, rock pools, compost heaps, and rotting logs are all habitats. Large habitats, like forests, mountains, and deserts are made up of smaller habitats. Each type of tree in a forest is a separate habitat and the carpet of leaves on the forest floor is another. In simple terms, a habitat is a place where an organism can feed, shelter, and reproduce.

In a park or large garden there can be a number of habitats. A large tree provides food for earthworms, woodlice, and other soil-based animals that feed on the dead leaves under the tree. Mosses, lichens, and sometimes ferns, can grow on the trunk of the tree. The tree provides shelter, as well as possibly

OXFORD
UNIVERSITY PRESS

nesting sites for birds. The birds eat the insects and other animals that feed on the leaves and flowers of the tree, or which use the crevices in its bark for shelter.

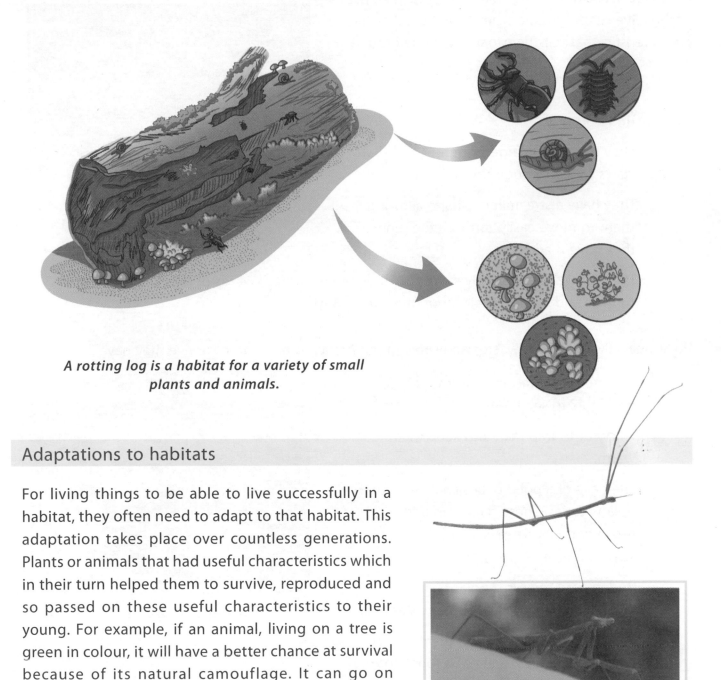

A rotting log is a habitat for a variety of small plants and animals.

Adaptations to habitats

For living things to be able to live successfully in a habitat, they often need to adapt to that habitat. This adaptation takes place over countless generations. Plants or animals that had useful characteristics which in their turn helped them to survive, reproduced and so passed on these useful characteristics to their young. For example, if an animal, living on a tree is green in colour, it will have a better chance at survival because of its natural camouflage. It can go on reproducing and pass on its distint characteristic to its young for another generation at least.

The stick insect/leaf insect is adapted to a life amongst twigs and leaves.

Here are some real examples of animals that have become adapted to their environments:

Moles are active burrowing animals that spend most of their lives underground. They have the following characteristics that help them to survive underground:

A mole

- They have a good sense of smell to detect the earthworms they feed on underground.

- They have extra-large front feet and sharp claws to dig through the soil.

- They have a streamlined shape allowing them to move easily through the tunnels they have made.

- Their fur is short and velvety so that they can move backwards or forwards in their tunnels and not rub their fur up the wrong way.

Polar bears live in the icy wastes and snow of the Arctic. To help them survive they have:

- A white coat that makes it less easy for predators to see them.

- Thick fur to trap heat and keep them warm.

- The hairs of a polar bear's coat are actually hollow tubes. These hairs trap and magnify the Sun's rays, which helps to keep the bear warm.

- Underneath the fur, a polar bear's skin is black, a colour which absorbs heat.

A polar bear on an ice floe

- Under its skin the bear has plenty of fat for insulation and to act as a food store.

- Sharp teeth for killing the seals on which they prey.

- Strong legs for walking and swimming long distances in search of food.

- Sharp claws and hairs on the soles of the feet to improve their grip on icy surfaces.

A fish living in a pond has:

- A streamlined body to make it easier to move through the water.

- Fins to help it swim through the water.

- A tail so that it can control the direction of its movement.

- Gills to absorb oxygen that is dissolved in the pond water.

- Overlapping scales on its body to keep the water out.

- A gas-filled bag called the swimbladder, inside its body to keep it afloat.

- Many fish have a slippery liquid called mucus, covering their scales. This helps the fish to slide through the water.

Freshwater fish

The cactus is adapted to living in hot, dry desert conditions. It has:

- Long, spreading roots to find water below the ground, so that water can be taken in quickly over a wide area before it drains away.

- Swollen stems to store as much water as possible.

- Leaves reduced to small spines, which not only reduces water loss by evaporation because their surface area is small, but also deters animals from eating the plant.

- The plant has a small surface area for its size, helping it to reduce water loss.

- It flowers after rain, producing seeds quickly before the next dry spell begins.

The spines are modified leaves.

Changing habitats

In nature, habitats change all the time. Some of these changes occur only occasionally. Forests and grasslands sometimes catch fire in hot weather. Rivers burst their banks and flood the surrounding land. Storms batter coral reefs and coasts. Some of the animals and plants that live in these habitats have adaptations that allow them to survive these sudden changes. Those that have not adapted become extinct in that particular habitat.

Daily changes

There are some changes to the habitat which occur daily and many species have adapted in ways that allow them to cope with these changes. Most plants have flowers that open during the day to allow them to be pollinated by insects. They close at night or when it rains, for protection. Many small **mammals**, such as mice, voles, and rabbits, come out only at night to avoid predators. However, some predators such as owls also come out at night. Many desert animals hide during the day to avoid the heat of the Sun, but come out at night to feed when it is cooler and when less water evaporates from their bodies.

Plants and animals living on the seashore have to be able to withstand the regular changes caused by high and low tides.

Seashores change every time the tide comes in and goes out. The animals living on beaches have to hide in the sand or mud until the tide returns. This is also the time that many wading birds search the mud and sand for these hidden animals. Animals living in rock pools have to be able to withstand the water becoming more and more salty after the tide has gone out, when water evaporates in the Sun. If there is a sudden downpour of rain, they have to be able to withstand the water in the rock pool rapidly becoming a more dilute salt solution.

OXFORD
UNIVERSITY PRESS

Seasonal changes

Many plants and animals also have to adapt to yearly changes in temperature, sunlight, and availability of food and water. **Deciduous** trees lose their leaves before the winter when there will be little sunlight, less water, and lower temperatures for photosynthesis to occur.

Deciduous trees, such as this oak, lose their leaves as winter approaches.

Flowers die off plants in winter because there are few insects to pollinate them. Many plants die down completely during the winter and remain dormant until the spring.

Some mammals grow thicker coats in the winter while a few living in snowy areas, including the stoat, Arctic hare, and Arctic fox, change colour for maximum camouflage. Some animals eat a lot in the autumn when there is plenty of food about, and then sleep or **hibernate** in the winter when food supplies are scarce. A few mammals and birds store food for the winter. Some insects hibernate while others spend the winter as **pupae**. Many birds fly away to warmer places in the winter where there is more food. This is called **migration**.

The Arctic tern makes the longest migration of any animal. The birds fly up to 80,000 km each year while migrating from the Arctic to the Antarctic and back again.

In the spring, many plants growing on the floor of deciduous woodlands or forests, flower and produce seeds quickly. They complete their life cycle before the leaves open on the trees above and the deep shade prevents them from carrying out photosynthesis.

Competition

All animals need food, water, and space if they are to survive. All plants need light, water, and space if they are to make their food by photosynthesis and survive. The members of a species have to compete with each other to make sure they each get enough of the things they need to survive on. They also have to compete with the members of other species who have the same needs.

If, for example, two species of animals are competing for grass and there is not much grass

If the weather turns dry and the grass begins to die, these herds of zebra and wildebeest will compete with each other. Only the strongest, fittest animals will survive.

available, some will starve because less food is available for each one of them. This competition limits the numbers of each species that can survive in a particular habitat. Many living things produce vast numbers of seeds or eggs. A single poppy, for example, can produce thousands of seeds while some fish lay millions of eggs. But usually the numbers of poppies and fish stay more or less the same. This is because the seedling poppies or young fish have to compete with their own kind, as well as with other species, for the things they need to survive on. Usually it is the strongest and fittest which survive.

Succession

Another type of change to habitats occurs as a result of competition over a long period of time. If a patch of ground is cleared of all the plants, it does not stay bare for long. Soon plants move in—the first are usually the quick-growing plants we call 'weeds'. These plants are soon followed by animals that can use the plants for food and shelter. After a time, larger, stronger plants will begin to colonise the area. They may include tall flowering plants or shrubs, which gradually cut off the light to the low-growing plants. Because the latter can no longer make their food, they soon die out. Over a long period of time, seedling trees will begin to grow on the area. As these trees grow, they will shade out the light and prevent other plants from growing. The result will be that the area is now woodland or forest. This type of change where one species replaces another is called succession

OXFORD
UNIVERSITY PRESS

Ecosystems

An **ecosystem** is made up of one or more habitats and the **communities** of plants and animals that live in them. An ecosystem includes the rocks and soil below the ground, the surface of the ground, and the air above it. The plants and animals in an ecosystem react with each other and with their surroundings. An ecosystem can be anything from a small piece of rotting log to a vast lake. Deserts, seashores, rivers, grasslands, oceans, and rainforests are just a few examples of the larger ecosystems.

River

Desert

Grassland

Tropical rainforest

These are some of the world's larger ecosystems.

Living things depend upon each other

Whether they are part of a habitat or an ecosystem, living things depend upon each other. You already know that animals depend upon plants for their food and the oxygen in the air they breathe. Because plants are almost the only living things which can make their own food, they are often called the **producers** of the world.

Nearly all other animals depend directly or indirectly upon plant food, and so they are called consumers. Herbivores such as cattle, sheep, rabbits, and camels are called primary consumers because they eat plant food. Carnivores such as foxes, leopards, lions, hawks, and eagles are called secondary consumers because they eat herbivores (and sometimes each other), and so depend indirectly on plants for food.

a. Producer
b. Herbivore or primary consumer
c. Carnivore or secondary consumer
d. Detritivore

When animals and plants die, their bodies decay and eventually disappear into the soil. The main decomposers which bring about decay are certain bacteria and fungi. Scavengers help to break down dead animals into smaller pieces, while the so-called detritivores such as earthworms, woodlice, millipedes, and slugs may break down dead plant materials into smaller pieces. Eventually, the dead material or the faeces or droppings of the animals that ate it, becomes food for bacteria and fungi. During the decay or decomposition process, the once-living material is broken down into humus in the soil. This then forms mineral salts which living plants can use to help make their food and grow.

In simple terms, sunlight provides energy which keeps all the animals on Earth alive, along with many fungi and bacteria. Producers convert sunlight energy into food, while consumers share this energy among themselves when they eat plants and each other. This flow of energy from producers to consumers leads to the formation of food chains and food webs.

OXFORD
UNIVERSITY PRESS

Food chains and food webs

A simple food chain is:

grass ⟶ rabbits ⟶ buzzards

This occurs when rabbits eat grass and buzzards eat rabbits. All food chains begin with green plants because these are the producers, while the other links in the chain are consumers.

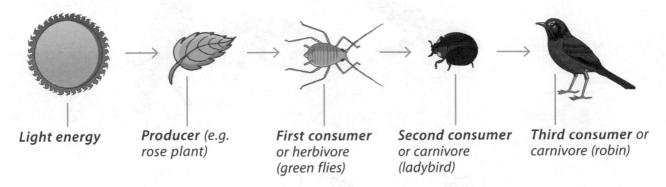

A simple food chain

Light energy   **Producer** (e.g. rose plant)   **First consumer** or herbivore (green flies)   **Second consumer** or carnivore (ladybird)   **Third consumer** or carnivore (robin)

Here is another food chain that might be found in a freshwater pond:

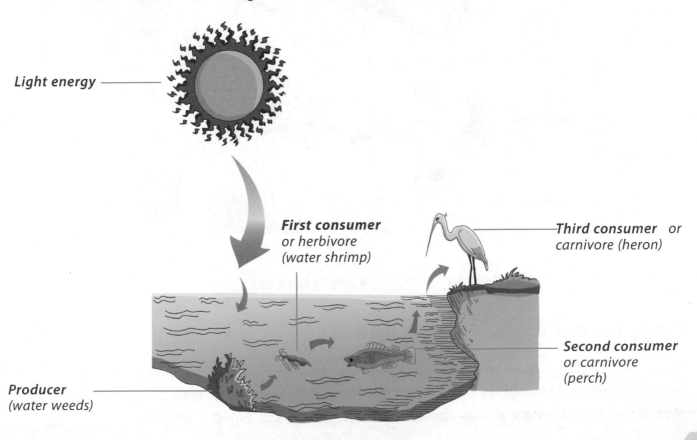

Light energy

First consumer or herbivore (water shrimp)

Third consumer or carnivore (heron)

Second consumer or carnivore (perch)

Producer (water weeds)

A freshwater pond food chain

Food webs

Food chains are rarely as simple as this, because even in the case of the example with grass, the rabbit, and buzzards—there are many other animals that eat grass besides rabbits and similarly many other animals eat rabbits besides buzzards. A truer summary of what happens in an ecosystem is a food web, where several food chains are connected together. The picture below shows a food web, but even this is a simplified version of what really happens in nature.

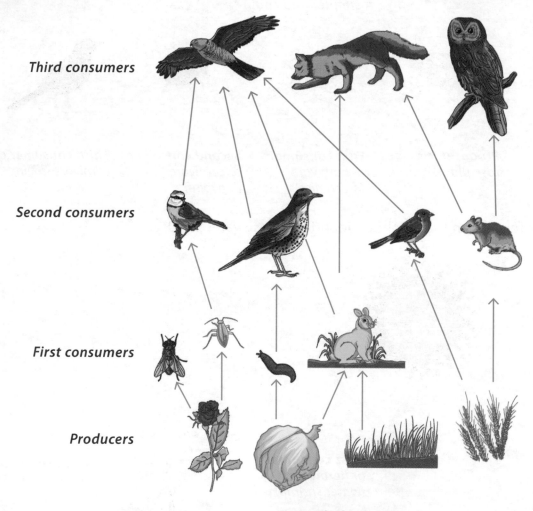

Third consumers

Second consumers

First consumers

Producers

A simple food web

Energy transfers in a food chain or food web

The arrows in a food chain or food web really show the direction in which energy moves from one organism to another. Food chains and food webs always start with green plants, the producers, as they are able to absorb some of the energy of sunlight directly.

OXFORD
UNIVERSITY PRESS

Only a small amount of the energy the plant takes in is passed on along the food chain. If we think of a food chain consisting of:

grass ───────────→ rabbit ───────────→ fox

one rabbit will eat a lot more than just one grass plant and, during its life, a fox will almost certainly eat more than one rabbit. We can show this relationship as a **pyramid of numbers**:

If all the energy in the grass was passed on to all the rabbits, and all the energy in the rabbits was passed on to the foxes, there would not be such a big change in the numbers of organisms between each level of the pyramid. However, the grass plants do not just use the energy of the Sun to allow them to grow—they also use it for other life processes such as respiration and reproduction. It is very unusual for more than 10 per cent of the energy in the plants to be passed on to the herbivore. The rabbit, the herbivore, is even more 'wasteful' of energy. Much of the energy the rabbit takes in from the grass is lost to its surroundings in the form of heat. Some energy is used up when the rabbit moves, while some is lost when it excretes or reproduces. This leaves very little energy (perhaps 5 to 10 per cent) for growth, which can then be passed on to the fox.

The reason, then, why food chains are short is because so much energy is lost at each stage for there to be more than one, two, or possibly three consumers after the green plant producer. This is also the reason why no animal specialises in preying on large carnivores such as tigers, jaguars, and polar bears. It is not because these animals are so fierce. It is because there just would not be enough of these animals around to provide food energy for some 'super carnivore'.

A pyramid of numbers

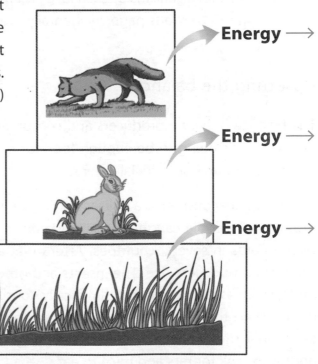

Energy is 'lost' at each level of the pyramid of numbers.

A few pyramids of numbers are a funny shape, as in the example below:

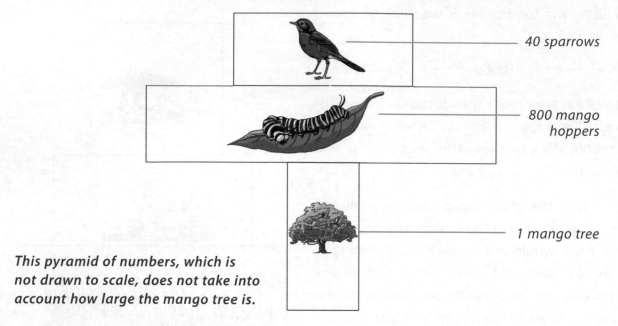

40 sparrows

800 mango hoppers

1 mango tree

This pyramid of numbers, which is not drawn to scale, does not take into account how large the mango tree is.

This 'pyramid' looks strange because the mango tree is very large compared with the size of the mango hoppers. There is only one mango tree, but there could be thousands of mango hoppers feeding on its leaves. If we changed the 'pyramid' so that it showed the total mass of the organisms at each level, then it would look more like the grass/rabbit/fox pyramid on the previous page. Incidentally, we would then have what is called a pyramid of biomass.

Upsetting the balance

The balance between producers and consumers in a food chain or food web is a delicate one if there is going to be enough food for everyone. The balance can easily be upset or broken by natural or artificial means.

Frogs' legs are considered a delicacy in France. To meet the demand for frogs' legs in French restaurants, people caught and killed large numbers of frog population living in the rice paddy fields in several countries. After quite a short period of time, the rice fields were producing much less rice. The insects and other invertebrate pests that the frogs had fed on had increased in numbers dramatically, consuming more of the rice plants. Another effect of upsetting the natural balance was that people saw more and more snakes. The reason being that the snakes, which had previously fed on frogs, were now coming to people's homes to look for rats and mice to eat.

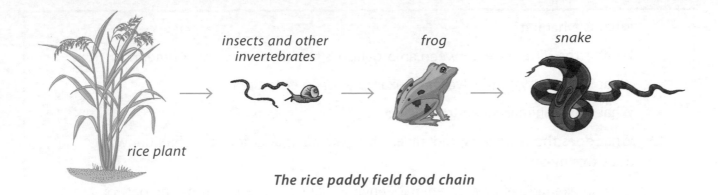

rice plant — *insects and other invertebrates* — *frog* — *snake*

The rice paddy field food chain

Poisons also build up as they pass along a food chain. DDT is a chemical that was once widely used to kill insect pests of crops. But in the 1960s, scientists discovered that the numbers of ospreys, hawks, eagles, and other birds of prey were decreasing dramatically. Eventually, they discovered that the bodies of the birds of prey contained large amounts of DDT. If the affected birds did lay eggs, the eggs had very thin shells which broke easily so that the developing baby birds were crushed in the nest.

The problem was that DDT was not **biodegradable**. It built up in the soil, and then was washed into rivers and seas. There, it was taken up by tiny plants (the phytoplankton) which were eaten by fish, the ospreys. On land, the DDT was taken up by small birds that ate the poisoned insects which ate the poisoned plants, and then were eaten by hawks and other larger birds of prey. The DDT did not affect the plants and animals low down in the food chains because it was at quite low concentrations. But large animals eat many smaller animals and so can take in large quantities of the poison. The result is that the poison becomes more and more concentrated in the bodies of animals further up the food chain.

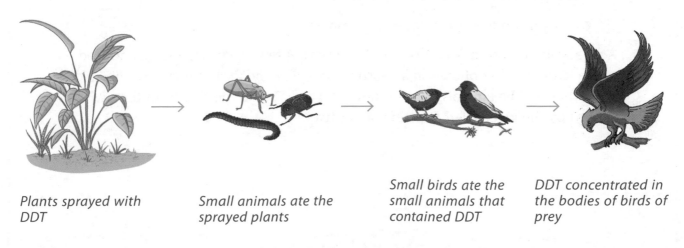

Plants sprayed with DDT

Small animals ate the sprayed plants

Small birds ate the small animals that contained DDT

DDT concentrated in the bodies of birds of prey

How DDT becomes concentrated along a food chain

Questions

1. What is a habitat?

2. What is the difference between an organism's habitat and its environment?

3. What is an ecosystem? Give three examples of an ecosystem.

4. What do all animals need to survive?

5. What does the word 'adapted' mean? If an animal is adapted to its habitat, what does this mean?

6. Give an example of how an animal's environment can change from one part of a day to another.

7. Give an example of how a plant's environment can change from season to season.

8. What limits the number of species that can survive in a habitat?

9. What do some animals do to survive at difficult seasons of the year?

10. Most flowers close up at night for protection, but a few flowers remain closed until dusk and then remain open till morning. Can you suggest reasons for this?

11. What are the two main groups of decomposers? How do decomposers obtain their energy?

12. Explain why life on Earth could not continue if there were no decomposers.

13. What do the arrows in a food chain or food web represent?

14. Why do most food chains have only two, three, or rarely, four consumers after the green plant producer?

15. What would be the effect on the plants and animals in a food chain if,

    i. the top predator increased in number;

    ii. the plant producers increased in number?

16. A weedkiller was sprayed onto a field of wheat. A few weeks later it was noticed that a large number of owls in a nearby wood were dying. The owls eat only mice and other small mammals, they do not eat wheat. Could the deaths of the owls be caused by the weedkiller? Explain your answer.

OXFORD
UNIVERSITY PRESS

Things to do

1. Make a list of all the foods you ate yesterday. Find out what kinds of animals or plants these foods came from. If the food came from animals, what kinds of foods did those animals eat? Write out food chains of the animal foods that you ate.

2. Devise an experiment whereby you could measure how much food is eaten by a small animal, such as a slug or snail. What type of food would you offer the animals? How would you make sure that they were hungry? What measurements would you make? What other precautions would be necessary? How would you record your results?

3. Look around your home or school. How many different food chains can you find? Write them out, joining the various stages with arrows.

4. Collect as many pictures as you can from magazines and divide them up into producers, consumers, and decomposers. How many food chains can you make from your pictures? Can you join the food chains to make a food web?

5. Use reference books, or the internet, to find out how a lion or an elephant is adapted to its environment.

Water, water everywhere

CHAPTER 7

Water and life

Water may appear to be just a colourless, odourless, and tasteless liquid, but it is one of the most important substances on Earth. Without drinking water, we would die. About 70 per cent of our body weight is water. People have lived for a month or more without food, but they can not survive more than three or four days without water. Every day we need to drink about 2 litres of water just to stay alive.

We wash our bodies, our clothes, and many other things with water. We use water to flush the toilet. The foods we eat have water in them, while all our drinks are largely water based. We use water to cook many of our foods. Water is also important for many leisure activities.

Many of our leisure activities take place on or in the water.

BASIC FACTS

- Roughly, three-quarters of the Earth is covered by water.
- Most (about 97 per cent) of the water on Earth is salty sea water.
- Only about 3 per cent of the world's water is fresh water and much of this is ice.
- The water cycle cleans or purifies the world's water supplies.
- Water is used in our homes, on farms, in industries, and for leisure activities.
- A great deal of water is used for irrigating crops.
- The bodies of plants and animals are largely water.
- The treatment of water for drinking involves filtering out the larger items of dirt, removing smaller suspended particles, and killing germs with chlorine.
- Sewage is the waste water from homes, schools, shops, and factories.
- At a sewage treatment works, the sewage is screened to remove the larger debris. Grit and sand are allowed to settle out. Then special bacteria feed on the liquid effluent, turning the waste matter into carbon dioxide and water.
- Salt can be removed from sea water by a process of distillation called desalination.
- A number of serious diseases can be spread by drinking or using dirty water.
- Water can be polluted by fertilizers and farm animal manure, chemical pesticides, waste chemicals, sewage, litter, oil, heat from power stations, and drainage water from landfill sites.
- Water is a precious commodity and we need to take care of supplies, especially where these supplies are limited.

OXFORD
UNIVERSITY PRESS

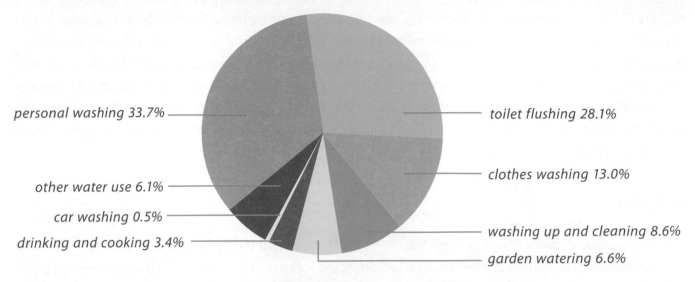

personal washing 33.7%

other water use 6.1%

car washing 0.5%

drinking and cooking 3.4%

toilet flushing 28.1%

clothes washing 13.0%

washing up and cleaning 8.6%

garden watering 6.6%

This chart shows the use of water for different activities in the average home in England. Notice that only a tiny part of the water is used for drinking and cooking, while most of it goes down the drain! How does this use of water compare with that in your home?

Animals, plants, and water

Animals and plants need water to live. Some simple plants and animals are 99 per cent water. Plants take up water from the soil through their roots. In just one day, a large deciduous tree can take in 20,000 litres of water from the soil. The animals that provide us with meat, milk, and eggs need large amounts of clean water to drink. A dairy cow, for example, may drink 135 litres of water a day. Water is also home to millions of plants and animals and it supplies us with one of our most important foods—fish.

Crops and irrigation

Farmers all around the world need water for their crops. In some places, where there is not much rain and the land is dry, farmers bring water from rivers, lakes, and wells to their fields. Water is carried in pipes and ditches. This special kind of watering is called irrigation. In Pakistan, 90 per cent of the water supplies are used for irrigation and other agricultural uses. Some crops need more water to grow than others. Rice and cotton, for example, can only be grown in countries that have a hot, wet climate.

This crop is being irrigated with water from a local river.

Although crops can grow well when they are irrigated, there can also be problems. Rainwater and water from wells or boreholes always contains some salts. If the soil is flooded with water, some of the water evaporates, leaving the salts behind. Eventually the soil becomes so salty that plants cannot grow because they cannot take up water by osmosis (page 33). This is particularly a problem when the climate is hot and the soil drainage is poor. The Pakistani government is investigating ways of irrigating crops, perhaps by drip-feeding the water onto the plants, so that less water is used and less salt accumulates.

Industry

Industry uses vast quantities of water. One of the most important uses of water is as a solvent because it dissolves so many other substances. In addition, some industries use water to cool the moving parts of machinery or hot substances. Water is also used to help produce most of our electricity. All power stations that burn fuels use water to make steam. This turns the machines that produce electricity. Water is also used for cooling. A large power station needs 200,000 litres of water every hour just to cool the steam and turn it back into water. In hydro-electric power stations, the water of fast-flowing rivers is used to turn the machines that produce electricity.

Water is also used to make many of the things we see or use every day. Making cement, concrete, steel, paper, and petroleum products uses huge quantities of water. Paper, for example, is made from a pulp of water and wood. Water is also used to make or process many kinds of food.

20,000 litres of water to make 1 tonne of steel

450,000 litres of water to make a small car

60 litres of water to make a pair of shoes

9 litres of water to make one comic

2.7 litres of water to make a 1 litre bottle of lemonade

3,200 litres of water to make a cotton shirt

200 litres of water to make a sweater

3.6 litres of water to make 1 litre of milk

257 litres of water to make 1 kg of chicken meat

75,000 litres of water to make 1 kg of beef

OXFORD
UNIVERSITY PRESS

Water everywhere

If you look at a globe or a map of the world, you will see that nearly three-quarters of the Earth is covered by water. There are five great oceans, the Atlantic, Pacific, Indian, Arctic, and Antarctic or Southern Ocean. The largest ocean in the world is the Pacific Ocean. It covers about a third of the surface of the Earth and its average depth is over 4000 metres. In spite of their vast size, all the oceans are connected to each other. This means that their waters are mixed together.

In addition to the oceans, there are seas. Some of these, such as the Arabian Sea and the Sargasso Sea, are parts of oceans. Other seas are surrounded by the continents and so are separate from the oceans. The Mediterranean Sea, Red Sea, and Black Sea are all surrounded by continents, although the Mediterranean does have a narrow opening into the Atlantic Ocean. The largest of the world's seas is the South China Sea.

The Earth as seen from space

The water in the oceans and seas is always salty. Some of this salt has come from volcanoes under the sea, but most of it has come from rocks on land. When rain falls, it dissolves some of the salt in the rocks. Rivers and streams dissolve even more of the salt and carry it down to the sea.

Fresh water

Besides oceans and seas, there is water in lakes, rivers, streams, and ponds. Most of the water we need for drinking, washing, cooking, and growing plants comes from lakes and rivers or from wells and boreholes. This is called fresh water because it is not salty like seawater.

Much fresh water is in the form of ice. Most of this ice is around the North and South Poles, where it forms the polar ice caps. Ice is also found on the tops of high mountains. Sometimes the ice flows down the mountainside like a slow-moving river, called a glacier. Most of Pakistan's water comes from the Indus River and its tributaries. These are fed by glaciers on the Himalayan Mountains.

Much of Pakistan's water comes from glaciers like this one in the Himalayas.

There are huge quantities of fresh water under the ground. Every time it rains, some of the water soaks into the ground and through tiny cracks in rocks. Sometimes the water flows as an underground river. There is also a small proportion of the world's water in the air. We can see some of it as clouds, but much of it is the invisible gas called water vapour.

Although there are huge quantities of water in the world, about 97 per cent of it is salty. Only about 3 per cent of the world's water is fresh from lakes, rivers, streams, ice, clouds, or water vapour.

The water supply

We need clean water for drinking, cooking, and washing. In one year, the average family of four uses about 180,000 litres of water. If we are to stay healthy, this water has to be clean and safe to use.

All the water we use comes from rain, ice, or snow. Some people get their water from a stream or well. However, in many places, including those that are densely populated such as towns and cities, streams and wells cannot provide enough water for the population. Water is therefore taken from lakes, rivers, or **reservoirs**. A reservoir is a large artificial lake made by building a **dam** across a river. Wherever possible, reservoirs are built high up in hills or mountains where they can be fed by clean rivers and streams. Alternatively, water is pumped from a borehole that penetrates deep into the ground, and then stored in a huge tank or reservoir until it is needed.

The Tarbela dam and reservoir were completed in 1976. The dam is 143 metres high and the reservoir has an area of 250 km². The reservoir controls flooding of the Indus River and provides water for irrigation and the production of hydroelectricity. Because the river carries large amounts of rock fragments from the glaciers which feed it, eventually this sediment will fill the reservoir. On the left is a picture of Tarbela dam taken from space by an astronaut.

OXFORD
UNIVERSITY PRESS

Water treatment

In the best water treatment works, water is pumped from the reservoir or storage tank into a treatment plant. On the way, the water passes through huge strainers which filter the larger particles from the water.

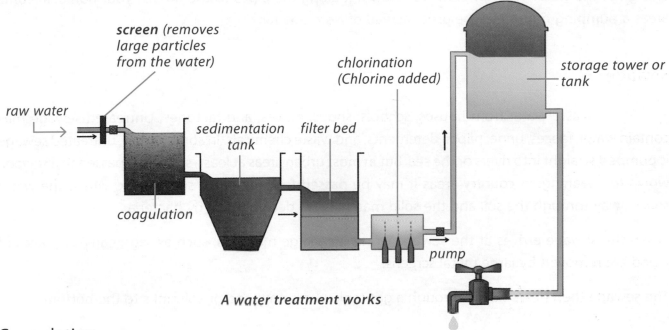

screen *(removes large particles from the water)*

chlorination (Chlorine added)

storage tower or tank

raw water

sedimentation tank

filter bed

coagulation

pump

A water treatment works

Coagulation

At the treatment plant, the raw water is mixed with alum (aluminium sulphate) and lime. The alum and lime make the tiny suspended particles of clay stick together.

Sedimentation

The water then goes to a sedimentation tank where the particles sink to the bottom of the tank from which they are removed. Because of the action of the lime and alum, the particles sink faster.

Filtration

Next, the water is passed through filter beds of sand and gravel. These remove the smaller particles of dirt.

Chlorination

Although the water now looks clear, it still contains harmful germs that are too small to be filtered out. Small doses of chlorine gas are added to the water to kill these germs. In some areas a chemical called flouride is also added to the water to help prevent tooth decay.

Storage

Now that the water is clean and germ-free, it is pumped along large underground pipes called water mains, to storage tanks. The tank supplying your area may be on a hill or at the top of a tall tower. This gives the water enough pressure to push it along the pipes to the taps in your home. In some areas a pumping house may be used instead of a storage tank.

Sewage

Sewage is waste water from houses, schools, shops, offices, and factories. Untreated sewage may contain water, faeces, urine, paper, detergents, and waste chemicals. In some places, untreated sewage is pumped straight into rivers or the sea. But in most urban areas at least, sewage is passed to a sewage works for cleaning. In country areas it may be passed to a cesspit or septic tank, where the water soaks away through the soil and the solid materials are decomposed by bacteria.

When the sewage arrives at the sewage works, any large materials, such as rags, cans, or pieces of wood are removed by large metal screens.

The sewage then flows slowly through a grit tank where any sand or soil sinks to the bottom.

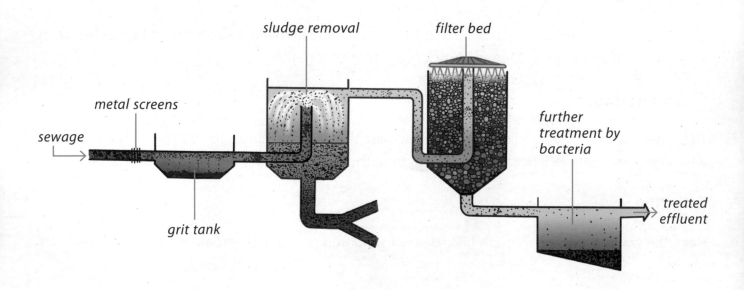

At a sewage treatment works, sewage is treated to make it clean and safe so that it can be returned to a river or the sea.

OXFORD
UNIVERSITY PRESS

Next the sewage flows into large tanks where the sludge (solid matter) settles to the bottom. From there it is scraped away by electric machinery.

The remaining liquid sewage, now called effluent, is often sprayed onto circular beds of stone, rock, or clinker. Sometimes it may be put into large tanks and have air blown through it. Either way, special bacteria feed on any waste matter in the effluent, turning it into harmless gases and water. The water is then clean enough to be returned to a river or pumped into the sea.

The sewage sludge is pumped to other tanks containing different kinds of bacteria. These destroy the unpleasant materials in the sludge and change them into the gas methane, which can be used as a fuel. Often the methane is used to produce all of the electricity needed by the sewage works. The 'digested sludge' is usually taken by trucks to be spread on farmland, where it acts as a fertilizer.

Distillation

The shortage of fresh water and the need for more clean water is already causing problems in many dry regions of the world. One way to obtain more fresh water is by **distillation**. This is very similar to the process nature uses to recycle water in what is called the **water cycle**. During the water cycle, the Sun makes water evaporate from the surface of oceans, seas, lakes, streams, and other moist surfaces. High in the sky, the water vapour eventually comes in contact with cooler air, where it condenses to form rain, hail, or snow. This falls and feeds rivers that eventually flow back into oceans, seas, and lakes.

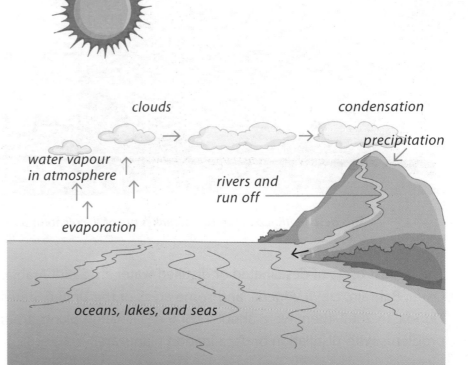

clouds

condensation

precipitation

water vapour in atmosphere

rivers and run off

evaporation

oceans, lakes, and seas

The water cycle converts salty or dirty water into clean water.

The process can be imitated artificially on a small scale, as well on as a large scale to remove the salt from sea water. This process is known as **desalination**. Today, desalination plants are used to turn sea water into drinking water on ships and in some dry regions of the world. Distillation can also be used to treat water in other areas where it has been fouled by natural and man-made pollutants.

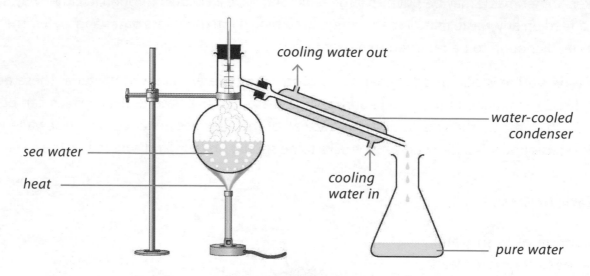

Distilling sea water

This desalination plant in Dubai makes use of the plentiful supplies of oil available locally.

The largest users of desalinated or distilled water are Saudi Arabia, Kuwait, the United Arab Emirates, Qatar, Bahrain, Libya, Algeria, and some areas of the United States, especially California and parts of Florida. In 2002, there were about 12,500 desalination plants around the world in 120 countries. The problems with distillation or desalination plants are:

- It is not cheap because it requires large quantities of fuel to heat the seawater. The countries which use desalination are mainly those with large quantities of oil available. In some countries, it may be possible to use wind or solar power to work desalination plants.

- Many of the substances such as pesticides which pollute water, have a lower boiling point than water and so can not be removed by ordinary distillation.

- Distilled water is pure and is not really suitable for drinking because it has a 'flat' taste and it lacks some of the important minerals that the body needs.

Safe water

We tend to take water for granted. We turn on a tap and we have water to drink or wash with. We flush the toilet and water washes away our wastes. But at least two-thirds of the people in the world do not have a tap inside their home. They have to obtain water from a tap outside their homes, wells, waterholes, streams or rivers. Their toilet may be a bucket, a hole in the ground, or a river or stream, and this water may be **polluted**

The unwanted substances in polluted water may also be harmful to plants and animals living in the water, as well as to the plants, animals, and people on land, who use the water or come into contact with it. Some of the pollutants that may find their way into rivers, streams, lakes, and wells are as follows:

Untreated sewage

The faeces and urine in untreated sewage may contain harmful germs. **Water-borne diseases** are spread by people drinking water that contain bacteria or viruses. Examples of diseases which are spread in this way include polio, hepatitis, cholera, and typhoid. Scientists believe that eight out of ten people in the less developed countries who are ill have a disease that has been spread by the water they drink or use.

Water-washed diseases are spread when people do not have enough water for washing hands and the rest of their bodies, and for washing kitchen pots and pans. Skin diseases, eye infections, and diarrhoea are examples of illnesses which spread rapidly when people are short of water. One common water-washed disease is trachoma, an eye disease which spreads rapidly in hot, dry climates when there is a shortage of water. The disease is caused by a bacterium which scars the eye and eventually causes blindness. Trachoma is one of the main causes of blindness. It could be prevented if people had plenty of water for washing, since the disease does not then spread so easily and can be cleared up with antibiotic ointment.

Water-related diseases are spread by animals such as snails or parasitic worms, which spend part of their lives in water or by insects such as mosquitoes, which breed in water. One of the worst water-related diseases is bilharzia or schistosomiasis. It is spread by parasitic worms which spend part of their lives in water snails. What happens is this. If infected human faeces are passed outdoors anywhere near water, the worm larvae enter water snails and multiply. The worm larvae get into the body of anyone drinking the water or enter through the skin of anyone washing, swimming, or wading in it. Inside the infected person's body, the parasitic worms cause many symptoms, including bleeding, pain, coughs, diarrhoea, fever, fatigue, sores, and enlargement of the liver and spleen.

Every day, about 70,000 children die from diseases spread by drinking or using bad water. This is caused not only by drinking water that has been polluted by human sewage, but also because of the shortage of water.

There are other effects of human sewage getting into lakes, rivers, and streams. Some of the substances in the sewage make algae grow rapidly. As more and more algae grow, they prevent light getting to other plants in the water, which then die. The algae use up oxygen when they die and rot away, leaving little for the fish and other wildlife, which are slowly suffocated.

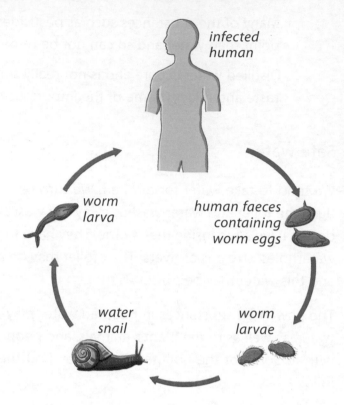

How bilharzia or schistosomiasis is spread

Fertilizers and farm animal manure

Excess fertilizers and animal manure, used to make crops grow better, can be washed into rivers and streams by rain. Both the fertilizers and manures can make algae grow and block the light from other water plants. As the algae die, the bacteria that decompose them break down the fertilizers, manure, and dead algae, using up all the oxygen as they do so. The original water plants die, as also do the fish and other water animals.

Chemical pesticides

Pesticides used on farms to get rid of insect pests and weeds can be washed into rivers and streams during heavy rain. Some of these chemicals are poisonous and they accumulate in the bodies of animals which drink the water or eat the contaminated water plants. The poisons are concentrated as they move along the various food chains (see page 69). The health of people who drink the water or eat fish containing the poisons can also be affected.

OXFORD
UNIVERSITY PRESS

Waste chemicals

Waste chemicals and poisonous metals such as mercury, can be discharged into rivers and lakes either accidentally or deliberately, by factories. These substances poison the fish in the water and the human beings who eat the fish. They also make the water unfit for people to use.

Litter

Waste paper, old cans, plastic bags, fishing lines, and other objects thrown by people into ditches, rivers, and the sea are not only unsightly, they can cause harm to wildlife. Turtles, for example, may swallow plastic bags, mistaking them for jellyfish.

Oil

From time to time oil is spilled from ships, either accidentally or deliberately when some oil tankers wash out their empty tanks at sea. Fish, seabirds, seals, dolphins, shellfish, and many other animals that swallow the oil can be poisoned. Sea birds that try to clean the oil from their feathers are also poisoned. Even if the birds have only a small amount of oil on them, the damaged feathers no longer keep the birds dry and warm and they die of cold. It takes many years for a stretch of coast to recover from an oil spill.

This swan has been coated with oil from an accidental spill at sea.

Power stations

Many power stations extract water to produce steam or for cooling purposes, before returning it at a much higher temperature to the river, lake, or sea it came from. Although the warm water does not actually pollute, it can harm water life as it contains less oxygen. It may also encourage algae to grow and be too warm for fish eggs to hatch.

Landfill sites

Poisonous substances from landfill sites can be washed into rivers by rainwater. These substances can harm wildlife and make the water unfit or dangerous for people to use.

Taking care of water

Whether we obtain our water from a tap or a well, it came originally from rain. The rain fell and some of the water sank into the ground, while some helped to make rivers and streams flow. People say that the world is fast running out of fresh water. That is not true, there is the same amount of water in the world now as there has always been. We are just making bigger and bigger demands on the water supplies we have.

Pakistan is one of the world's driest countries with average rainfall of under 240 mm a year. Almost two-thirds of that rain falls in the summer months of July to September. More than 90 per cent of Pakistan's water resources are used for irrigating crops and other agricultural needs. That leaves less than 10 per cent of the water for industry and for people to use for drinking, washing, cleaning, and disposing of sewage. To make matters worse, global warming is melting the glaciers in the Himalayas which feed the Indus River and its tributaries, from which most of Pakistan's water is obtained. River levels have dropped by two-thirds in the last 40 years, partly because of the melting of the glaciers and partly because more and more water is being taken for human use.

Obviously we must do everything we can not to waste water. Here are some things that you can do to reduce the amount of water you use without harming the environment too much:

- One third of all the water we use each day is flushed down the toilet. Ask your parents to put a brick in the cistern so that you will not flush so much water down the toilet each time.

- Do not waste food, because large amounts of water are needed to produce all of the foods we eat.

- A shower uses much less water than a bath, and it saves energy as well.

- Clean your teeth from a tumbler of water rather than from a running tap.

- Make sure the detergents you use for washing your clothes and dishes, and cleaning the bath, sink, and toilet are biodegradable. This will keep your waste water cleaner.

- Save water in dry weather by using cold washing-up water for your garden or house plants. Pour the water on the soil and not on the plants.

- Collect and store rainwater and use it for watering plants, washing cars, and for other jobs where drinking water is not necessary.

- Wash the car with a bucket of water, rather than with a hose.

- Do not pour waste oil, or any other harmful chemicals, down the drain.

- If you are out in the country, do not go to the toilet anywhere near a stream, ditch, lake or river.

- Do not drop litter anywhere.

- Reuse or recycle as many objects and materials as you can. Reduce the amount of waste of all kinds that you produce. This saves water and energy supplies.

OXFORD
UNIVERSITY PRESS

Questions

1. How is water important to

   i. plants,

   ii. animals, including humans?

2. What are the main uses of water in the home?

3. In your own words, describe how the water cycle cleans and purifies the water we use.

4. Why does the level of the sea remain roughly the same?

5. What are the main uses of water in industry? Give examples of each use.

6. What kinds of water animals and plants are useful to us as food?
   Make a table of all the examples you can think of.

7. Work with a friend. Discuss why water from a deep well is safer than water from a shallow well or a waterhole. Write down your conclusions.

8. What is the difference between sewage and a sewer? Write a sentence or two about each word to show you know what it means. How is sewage in the sea harmful? Use reference books, or the internet, to help you find out.

9. What would happen to the amount of water trapped as ice If our planet became

   i. hotter

   ii. colder

   Suggest how this would affect the water cycle.

10. Why do we need to save or conserve water? List five different ways of conserving water.

1. How much of your body weight is water? Weigh yourself in kilograms. Divide your weight by 10, and then multiply your answer by 7. How much water is there in your body? Compare your answer with those of your friends.

2. At a waterworks, dirty water is filtered using beds of sand and gravel. Mix a little soil in a jug of water to make the water dirty. Experiment and find the best material for filtering the dirty water to make it clean again. Materials you could try include, coffee filter papers, cotton wool, and nylon tights. Do NOT drink this filtered water.

3. Calculate how much water a dripping tap wastes. Turn on the cold tap until it is just dripping. Put a bucket under the tap and measure how much water drips into the bucket in an hour. Calculate how much water would drip away in a day, a week, and a year.

4. How is water used for people to enjoy themselves in your area? Make a list of the places where water is used for leisure activities. Draw pictures to show the different places.

5. Keep a diary of all the ways you use water during the whole day. Examples include washing your hands, flushing the toilet, and watering plants. Record your results as a histogram or pie chart.

6. A terrible disease called cholera struck parts of London in 1854. Hundreds of people died. A local doctor, John Snow, was able to prove it was because people drank dirty water. Find out more about cholera from reference books or the internet.

7. Make a sketch plan of your school and its grounds. Walk around the school and mark on your plan all the places where water moves, including any taps, stopcocks, gutters, and downpipes.

8. Some newspapers show the daily amount of rainfall for large towns and cities. Collect these figures for a week and record them on a chart. Make a league table with the wettest town at the top and the driest at the bottom. Use an atlas to help you mark these towns and cities on a map. What do you notice?

OXFORD
UNIVERSITY PRESS

Atoms

CHAPTER 8

BASIC FACTS

- An atom is the smallest part of an element which can exist.
- A chemical symbol represents one atom of an element.
- A chemical formula represents one molecule of an element or compound.
- All atoms consist of three particles: electrons, protons, and neutrons.
- The centre of an atom is called the nucleus.
- Different elements have different numbers of protons in their atoms.
- Electrons are arranged in energy levels or 'shells' around the nucleus of an atom.
- The atomic number of an element is the number of protons contained in one atom of the element.
- The mass number of an element is the total number of protons and neutrons in one atom of the element.
- Atoms are linked together in molecules by chemical bonds.
- An ion is a charged particle formed when an atom (or group of atoms) gains or loses one or more electrons.
- An ionic bond is a chemical bond formed by the transfer of one or more electrons from the outer shell of a metal atom to the outer shell of a non-metal atom.
- Ionic compounds are usually solids that will only melt at a very high temperature.
- A covalent bond is a chemical bond formed when atoms share their outermost electrons.
- The molecules formed when atoms are held together by covalent bonds can contain a small number of atoms, such as water and carbon dioxide, or a very large number of atoms, such as those in polythene and polystyrene.
- The valency of an element in a compound is the number of chemical bonds which one atom of the element can form in one molecule of the compound.
- Valencies are always small whole numbers.
- The valency of an element can often be seen from the formula of a compound containing that element.
- Isotopes are different forms of an element with different mass numbers.
- Radioisotopes are used in nuclear power stations, nuclear weapons, industry, medicine, and agriculture.

Everything around you is made up of tiny particles called atoms. This book, the trees outside, the room you are in, the Sun, the stars, the Moon are all made of atoms. Even your body is made of atoms, mainly atoms of the elements carbon, oxygen, hydrogen, and nitrogen. You do not look like any of these elements because atoms can form many different materials, depending on the way they are joined together.

Although these models are both made from the elements carbon, hydrogen, and oxygen—the elements are put together in two different ways.

You are probably familiar with the little plastic building blocks that can be easily joined together with a push or separated with a pull. Those blocks are made of a plastic called polyester. Polyester is made up of the elements carbon, hydrogen, and oxygen. Wood, a completely different material, is also made of carbon, hydrogen, and oxygen. But in wood the elements are put together in a different way to give a totally new material with a completely different appearance and properties.

Discovering atoms

A Greek philosopher, Democritus (c. 460-361 BC), first put forward the idea of atoms. He ground up different materials until he had a fine powder which could not be broken down any smaller. 'Atom' is the ancient Greek word for 'indivisible'.

In 1808, an English chemist, John Dalton, suggested from the experiments he had carried out that each chemical element is made up of different atoms and that elements are different because they are made of different atoms.

In 1911, the New Zealand-born physicist, Ernest Rutherford, discovered that atoms have a tiny dense nucleus.

Inside an atom

Although the word atom means 'indivisible', we now know that an atom is, in fact, made up of even smaller particles. If we could pull an atom apart, we would see that it is made up of three important particles. These are called **protons**, **neutrons**, and **electrons**. Different atoms are made up of different numbers of these three particles. Every atom contains a **nucleus**, usually made up of protons and neutrons. Electrons move rapidly around the nucleus.

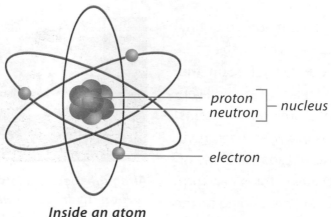

Inside an atom

OXFORD
UNIVERSITY PRESS

If an atom was enlarged until it was the size of a football pitch, the nucleus would be the size of a pinhead on the centre spot. Most of an atom is, in fact, empty space.

Protons and neutrons are about the same mass, but electrons are much lighter. Protons and electrons both carry a tiny electrical charge with the proton having a positive (+) charge, while the electron has an equal, but negative charge (–). Neutrons are neutral and carry no charge at all. An atom that has equal numbers of protons and electrons is electrically neutral.

Atoms and elements

A material that is made up of only one type of atom is called an **element**. So far, 117 elements have been discovered. Some of these are very rare, some are man-made, while other elements such as copper, sodium, and chlorine are common.

Atoms differ from one another because they are made up of different numbers of protons, neutrons, and electrons. The smallest atom of all is that of the gas hydrogen. This has only one proton and one electron. The largest naturally occurring atom that we know about is uranium. This has 92 protons and 92 electrons. It is the number of protons that makes the difference between the atoms. This number is called the **atomic number** and each element has a different atomic number.

Because there are always the same number of protons and electrons in an atom, if we know the atomic number, we also know how many electrons an atom has. It is the way the electrons are arranged around the nucleus which determines the properties of an atom or of an element of which it is a part.

Electrons and shells

Drawings of atoms, like the one on the pevious page, usually show electrons orbiting the nucleus rather like planets orbiting the Sun. This is not really a true picture of how electrons orbit the nucleus.

Electrons are not solid balls, but bundles of energy that move almost as fast as light. We have no idea where they are at any one instant. However, we do know that the electrons whizz around the nucleus of the atom in different layers called **shells**

The shells are arranged around the nucleus of the atom in energy levels. When we draw an atom, we show these energy levels or shells as circles around the nucleus. The nearer a circle is to the nucleus, the lower the energy level. The lowest energy shell, the one nearest the nucleus, is called the K shell. It can hold either one or two electrons.

The second shell, with the second energy level, is called the L shell. It can hold up to eight electrons.

The third energy level, the M shell, can also hold a maximum of eight electrons.

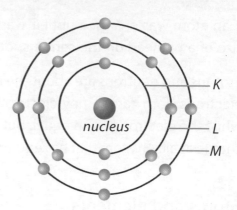

Filling electron levels

In an atom, the electrons fill the energy levels starting from the lowest energy level (K). When this is full with two electrons, the next electron goes into the L shell. When the L shell is full with eight electrons, then the electrons begin to fill the M energy level.

We have already seen that, as there are always the same number of protons and electrons in an atom, the atomic number also tells us how many electrons an atom has. Carbon, for example, has an atomic number of 6. It has 6 protons and 6 neutrons in its nucleus and 6 electrons orbiting the nucleus. 2 of these electrons will occupy the K shell, while the remaining 4, the L shell.

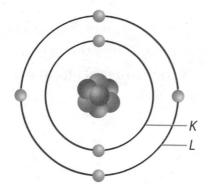

The arrangement of electrons around the nucleus of a carbon atom

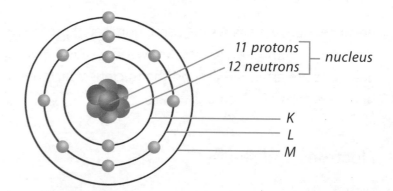

The sodium atom

A slightly more complicated example is that of the sodium atom. It has an atomic number of 11 and an atomic mass of 23. Thus, each sodium atom consists of 11 protons, 12 neutrons, and 11 electrons.

In the sodium atom there are two electrons in the K energy shell, eight electrons in the L shell, and the remaining one electron is in the outer M shell. The electron arrangement for the sodium atom is:

K L M
2 8 1

The number and arrangement of electrons in an atom is important because it controls the chemical properties of the atom. Elements such as sodium, with only one electron in the highest energy shell (M) of their atoms, are very reactive.

The table below shows how electrons are arranged in 20 elements:

Element	Symbol	Atomic number	Number of electrons	First shell	Second shell	Third shell	Fourth shell
hydrogen	H	1	1	1			
helium	He	2	2	2			
lithium	Li	3	3	2	1		
beryllium	Be	4	4	2	2		
boron	B	5	5	2	3		
carbon	C	6	6	2	4		
nitrogen	N	7	7	2	5		
oxygen	O	8	8	2	6		
fluorine	F	9	9	2	7		
neon	Ne	10	10	2	8		
sodium	Na	11	11	2	8	1	
magnesium	Mg	12	12	2	8	2	
aluminium	Al	13	13	2	8	3	
silicon	Si	14	14	2	8	4	
phosphorus	P	15	15	2	8	5	
sulphur	S	16	16	2	8	6	
chlorine	Cl	17	17	2	8	7	
argon	Ar	18	18	2	8	8	
potassium	K	19	19	2	8	8	1
calcium	Ca	20	20	2	8	8	2

Mass number and isotopes

Protons and neutrons have mass. The more neutrons there are in an atom, the heavier it is. This affects the density and other physical properties of the element. However, neutrons do not have an electrical charge and they do not affect the chemical properties of an element. To find out how many neutrons there are in a nucleus, we need to know the mass number of the atom. This tells us how many neutrons and protons there are in the nucleus. Here are a few examples:

Element	Atomic number (number of protons)	Mass number	Number of neutrons
hydrogen	1	1	0
carbon	6	12	6
nitrogen	7	14	7
oxygen	8	16	8
sodium	11	23	12
gold	79	197	118

All atoms of a particular element have the same number of protons (called the atomic number). However, they may have a different number of neutrons. A carbon atom always has 6 protons, but the number of neutrons can be 6, 7, or 8. Because neutrons do not affect the chemical properties of an atom, all types of carbon atoms have the same chemical properties.

These different versions of the same element are known as isotopes. Scientists name isotopes by putting the mass number (the number of protons and neutrons) after the name of the element, for example uranium-235. In this case, the total number of neutrons and protons in the nucleus is 235.

The commonest isotope of the element carbon is carbon-12, which has 6 protons, 6 neutrons, and 6 electrons, and a mass number of 12. It makes up nearly 99 per cent of all the carbon on Earth. There are two other isotopes of carbon: carbon-13 has 6 protons, 7 neutrons, and 6 electrons, and a mass number of 13. It makes up just over 1 per cent of all the world's carbon. Carbon-14, which is even rarer, has 6 protons, 8 neutrons, and 6 electrons.

Different isotopes of the same element behave in the same way in chemical reactions, although they may have different physical properties. All three isotopes of carbon, for example, can combine with oxygen to form carbon dioxide, but only carbon-14 is radioactive.

OXFORD
UNIVERSITY PRESS

Radioisotopes

Most atoms are stable, but a few are not. Unstable atoms break up into smaller, more stable atoms. As they break up, radiation is released in a process called radioactive decay. Unstable atoms are radioactive and we call them radioisotopes. As we saw with carbon-14, the unstable nuclei of radioisotopes have a different number or neutrons from stable isotopes. The larger the number of protons, neutrons, and electrons in an atom, the more likely it is to be radioactive. Uranium-238, for example, has 92 protons, 146 neutrons, and 92 electrons. It is highly radioactive. Of the three isotopes of carbon, only carbon-14 is radioactive.

Uses of radioisotopes

Radioactive substances give off particles and rays that can be harmful to living things. But radioactivity can also be useful. We use radioactivity to help produce electricity. We also use it in medicine, industry, and agriculture.

Atomic energy

The energy from the breakdown of some radioisotopes can be used. When the atoms of uranium-235 are bombarded with neutrons, they break down, producing nuclear or atomic energy. Each collision releases energy. In nuclear weapons, this energy is released all at once and causes great destruction. In a nuclear power station, the reaction is carefully controlled. The energy is released slowly as heat which turns water into steam. The steam is used to turn a turbine connected to a generator and this produces electricity. Some nuclear power stations use an artificial radioisotope, plutonium-239, instead of uranium.

This power station uses nuclear or atomic energy to turn water into steam. The steam turns turbines connected to electrical generators.

Medical uses

Each time a radioisotope decays naturally, it releases a small amount of energy. This can be used to produce a small electric current. Such nuclear batteries have a long life and can be very small. They can be used in a heart pacemaker (page 27). The pacemaker is placed inside the chest where it delivers a small, regular electric shock to the heart to keep it beating.

Tiny amounts of radioisotopes can be injected into, or swallowed by a patient. The path the isotope takes inside the body can then be traced on a computer screen. The activity of the organs can be studied in this way. Certain strong radioisotopes can be used to destroy cancer cells inside the body without the use of surgery. Many medical instruments can be sterilised using radiation.

Industrial uses

Radioisotopes are often used in industry. Gamma rays, one kind of nuclear radiation, can penetrate metals easily. They can be used to check for leaks in pipes, as well as to show up cracks and faults in metal objects. Since thick sheets of materials allow less radioactivity to pass through than thinner sheets, they can be used to check and control the thickness of materials.

Agricultural uses

Radioisotopes can be used to trace the path of an element through a plant. For example, to find out what happens to ordinary phosphorus when it is absorbed by plant roots, radioactive phosphorus, phosphorus-32, can be added to a phosphate fertilizer. Chemically the P-32 atoms behave in exactly the same way as the non-radioactive P-31 atoms in the fertilizer. The P-32 acts as a marker and so the path the phosphorus takes from the soil into the roots, up the stem, and into the leaves and flowers can be followed. The changes that occur inside a plant during photosynthesis can also be studied by labelling carbon dioxide gas with atoms of the radioactive form of carbon, C-14.

Ions and bonding

In an atom, the protons have positive electrical charges. These are balanced by the negative electrical charges of the electrons. The atom is, therefore, electrically neutral. However, if you add or take away one or more electrons from the outer shell of an atom, it becomes either negatively or positively charged. Such charged particles are called ions. The atom that has gained electrons is called an anion, and has a negative charge. The atom that has lost electrons is called a cation, and has a positive charge.

OXFORD
UNIVERSITY PRESS

If you combine sodium and chlorine atoms, you can make a chemical substance called sodium chloride—common salt. But common salt is not made just by mixing the atoms together. They are stuck together with a chemical 'glue' called a **bond**. All bonding involves the movement of electrons in the outermost shells of the atoms. But atoms use electrons to bond in different ways.

Ionic bonding

When salt is made, the sodium atoms each give an electron to a chlorine atom. When this happens, the atoms become ions. The sodium ion has a positive charge (it is a cation). When a chlorine atom gains an electron, it becomes a chloride ion which has a negative charge (it is an anion). The ions are attracted to each other very strongly because opposite electrical charges attract. This is known as **ionic bonding**. Most ionic bonds are very difficult to break. Ionic compounds are usually solids that will only melt at a very high temperature.

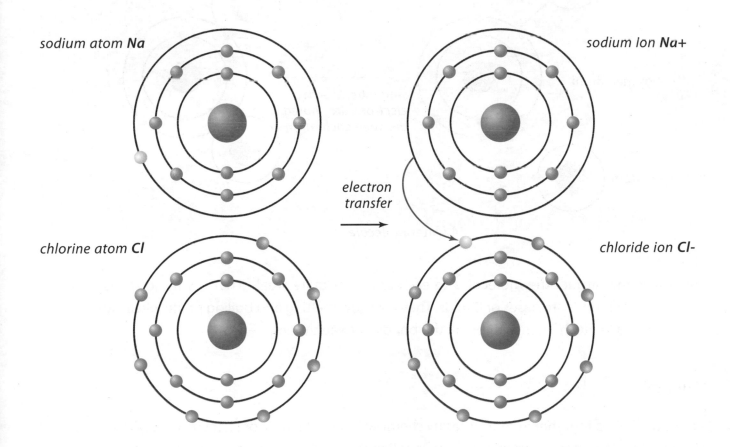

sodium atom Na

sodium Ion Na+

electron transfer

chlorine atom Cl

chloride ion Cl-

How the movement of an electron takes place to form sodium chloride

Covalent bonding

A lot of atoms do not easily lose or gain electrons to form ionic bonds. Instead, they share electrons between them. The electrons are shared in pairs called electron pairs. This type of bond is known as a covalent bond. A vast number of compounds have their atoms held together by covalent bonds, including most of the chemicals found in living things. The molecules formed when atoms are held together by covalent bonds can contain a small number of atoms such as water and carbon dioxide, or a very large number of atoms such as those in polythene and polystyrene. Some elements exist as molecules with the atoms held together by covalent bonds. Oxygen gas, for example, is made up of molecules each formed from two atoms.

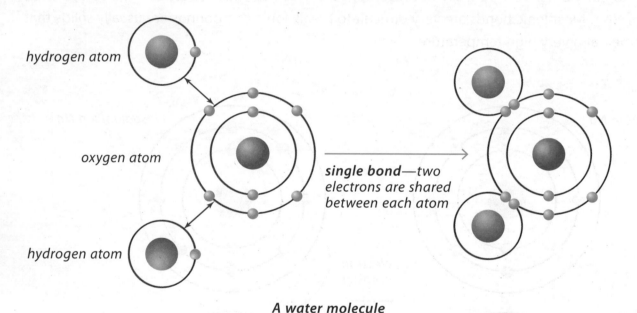

hydrogen atom

oxygen atom

single bond—two electrons are shared between each atom

hydrogen atom

A water molecule

The forces that attract the molecules to each other are quite weak. That is why so many covalent compounds are gases or liquids. They have low melting and boiling points because it does not take much energy to break the bonds between them.

Valency

Atoms are linked together in molecules by chemical bonds, such as ionic or covalent bonds. The number of bonds an atom can form is called its **valency**. Carbon, for example, has a valency of 4. In the methane gas, each carbon atom is bonded to four hydrogen atoms. Each hydrogen atom forms one bond, because hydrogen has a valency of 1.

It sometime helps to think of each atom having hooks coming from it which represent the valency bonds.

Here are the valencies of some elements which you will meet quite often. Valencies are always small whole numbers. The inert or rare gases such as helium and neon have zero valencies because they are unreactive and do not normally form compounds. That is the reason they are often referred to as the inert gases.

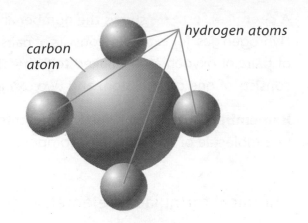

A molecule of methane

metals			non-metals		
name	symbol	valency	name	symbol	valency
sodium	Na	1	helium	He	0
potassium	K	1	neon	Ne	0
silver	Ag	1	hydrogen	H	1
calcium	Ca	2	chlorine	Cl	1
magnesium	Mg	2	bromine	Br	1
zinc	Zn	2	iodine	I	1
aluminium	Al	3	oxygen	O	2
			nitrogen	N	3
			carbon	C	4

Chemical formulae

To sum up what we have learnt so far about elements. There are more than hundred elements of which about ninety are found in nature. An element such as carbon, hydrogen, oxygen, gold, or iron cannot be split into simpler substances by ordinary chemical means. Each element has its own kind of atom which behaves in a particular way. Each element is represented by a symbol, such as C for carbon, Na for sodium, and Fe for iron. Some elements and many compounds consist of groups of atoms linked together. These groups of atoms are called molecules.

A **chemical formula** shows the number and kinds of atoms contained in a molecule of a substance. Hydrogen gas, for example, consists of pairs of hydrogen atoms linked together, while oxygen consists of pairs of oxygen atoms linked together. The smallest particle of the gas carbon dioxide, however, consists of one carbon atom and two oxygen atoms. It has the formula CO_2.

Remember: A chemical symbol represents one atom of an element. A chemical formula represents one molecule of an element or compound.

Chemical formulae of elements

For elements like oxygen and hydrogen which exist as molecules, the formula is the symbol of the element with the number of atoms in one molecule of the element, written at the bottom right-hand corner of the symbol. So, H_2 represents one molecule of hydrogen, while O_2 represents one molecule of oxygen. If we see 2H written, it means that there are two separate atoms of hydrogen, while 2O shows that there are two separate atoms of oxygen.

Chemical formulae of compounds

While there are only 117 chemical elements, scientists have found or made more than 26 million different compounds, many of them in the last eighty years or so. You could not possibly learn the names of all of these compounds, but if you know the chemical formulae of them, you can see what atoms are contained in one molecule of each substance. Chemical formulae are the chemist's shorthand writing.

Water, for example, is a compound of hydrogen and oxygen. The smallest 'bit' of water that can exist is a molecule of water. This is made up of two hydrogen atoms linked to one oxygen atom. It has the formula H_2O.

In a similar way, the carbon dioxide molecule is the smallest 'bit' that can exist. It consists of one atom of carbon linked to two atoms of oxygen, and has the formula CO_2. Notice that in the case of both the water and the carbon dioxide formulae, the '1' for the atom of hydrogen and the '1' for the atom of carbon are never written.

Here is the chemical formula for sulphuric acid:

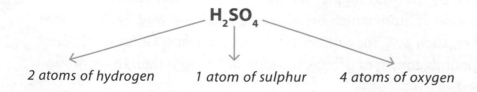

$$H_2SO_4$$

2 atoms of hydrogen   1 atom of sulphur   4 atoms of oxygen

OXFORD
UNIVERSITY PRESS

Sometimes brackets are used in the chemical formulae of compounds. These show that everything inside the brackets is multiplied by the number immediately after the brackets. This is the formula for calcium hydroxide.

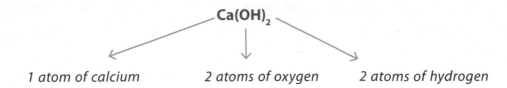

$$Ca(OH)_2$$

1 atom of calcium   *2 atoms of oxygen*   *2 atoms of hydrogen*

In the case of calcium hydroxide, then, there are two groups of OH.

Some common ions

Positive ion or anion	Valency	Formula	Negative ion or cation	Valency	Formula
sodium	1	Na^+	chloride	1	Cl^-
potassium	1	K^+	iodide	1	I^-
silver	1	Ag^+	hydroxide	1	NO_3^-
hydrogen	1	H^+	nitrate	1	H^+
ammonium	1	NH_4^+	bicarbonate	1	HCO_3^-
copper I	1	Cu^+	oxide	2	O_2^-
magnesium	2	Mg^{2+}	sulphide	2	S_2^-
calcium	2	Ca^{2+}	carbonate	2	CO_3^{2-}
copper II	2	Cu^{2+}	sulphate	2	SO_4^{2-}
lead II	2	Pb^{2+}	phosphate	3	PO_4^{3-}
zinc	2	Zn^{2+}			
iron II	2	Fe^{2+}			
aluminium	3	Al^{3+}			
iron III	3	Fe_3^+			

Remember that when you want to work out the formula for a chemical substance, positive ions will react with negative ions and vice versa. For example:

sodium + chloride ⟶ sodium chloride

Na+ + Cl⁻ ⟶ NaCl (common or table salt)

As was mentioned previously, you may find that it helps to think of the sodium ion having a single hook coming from it (its valency is 1) and linking up with the chloride ion with another single hook coming from it, as its valency is also 1.

Calcium carbonate (chalk or limestone) is slightly more difficult, since both the calcium ion and the carbonate ion have valencies of 2:

Calcium + carbonate $\longrightarrow$ **calcium carbonate**

$Ca_2^+ + CO_3^{2-} \longrightarrow CaCO_3$

Again, think of the calcium ion as having two hooks and the carbonate ion also having two hooks coming from it.

The law of constant composition

You have just been reading some of the most difficult parts of chemistry to understand. However, these studies on the composition of materials began a long time ago. As we saw on page 88, a Greek philosopher, Democritus (c. 460–361 BC), first put forward the idea of atoms. Chemistry as a true science began in the 18th century with the study of gases and burning. The properties of gases such as hydrogen and oxygen were carefully studied and the use of sensitive weighing machines helped scientists to measure accurately the changes in weight which occur during chemical changes.

By the beginning of the 19th century, two important laws of chemistry had been discovered. One was the *law of conservation of matter* which says that matter can neither be created nor destroyed, it is simply changed from one form to another. The second law is called the *law of constant composition*. This summarizes the results of many experiments and states that a chemical compound always contains the same constituents in the same proportions by weight. For example, no matter where it comes from or how it was produced, water always consists of one-ninth hydrogen to eight-ninths oxygen by weight. This discovery provided the first experimental evidence for the theory that all matter consists of atoms.

Questions

1. Describe what you understand by an element. Make sure that the word 'atom' or 'atoms' appears in your answer.

2. What is meant by: a) an atom? b) a molecule? c) a chemical bond? d) valency?

3. Explain the difference between atomic mass and atomic number.

4. What is a symbol? Give three examples of symbols.

5. Draw a table to show the differences between electrons, neutrons, and protons.

6. What name is given to the number of protons in a particular atom?

7. The chemical formula for glucose is $C_6H_{12}O_6$. How many atoms does a molecule of glucose contain and what are they?

8. The chemical formula for sulphuric acid is H_2SO_4. What is the total number of atoms in this molecule and what are they?

9. What are the properties of ionic compounds?

10. What are the properties of covalent compounds?

11. What is an isotope? Give two examples of elements which have isotopes.

12. How many ways can you think of in which we use radioisotopes?

Things to do

1. Use the information in the table of ions on page 99 to write out the formulae for: sodium carbonate, silver nitrate, sodium bicarbonate, aluminium oxide, and zinc carbonate.

2. Refer to the table on page 91, showing how electrons are arranged in the atoms of twenty common elements. Use that information to draw diagrams showing the atomic structure of each of the twenty elements.

3. For one week, collect as many newspaper and magazine articles as you can which contain information about nuclear energy or radioactivity. How many of the articles were about the negative effects of nuclear energy and radioactivity? How many articles were about the positive effects? What sort of things do people worry about when thinking of nuclear energy and radioactivity? Ask friends and family.

OXFORD
UNIVERSITY PRESS

Physical and chemical changes

CHAPTER 9

BASIC FACTS

- The three states of matter are solid, liquid, and gas.
- The existence of the three states of matter depends upon how strongly the particles they are made of, stick together.
- Particles are usually arranged regularly in a solid, but irregularly in liquids and gases.
- In a physical change, no new substance is formed.
- Physical changes do not involve a change in mass; the particles of the substance are rearranged without altering any chemical bonds.
- In a chemical change or chemical reaction, one or more new substances are formed.
- In a chemical reaction, no mass is lost when the reactants change into products.
- Chemical changes are permanent and they always involve a change in energy, usually heat energy.
- Exothermic reactions give out heat energy.
- Endothermic reactions take in heat energy.
- Fuel is a material which burns to produce energy, usually in the form of heat.
- Most fuels are hydrocarbons such as wood, coal, oil, and natural gas.
- Combustion is burning—a fuel reacts with oxygen to release useful energy.
- Fuel, heat, and oxygen are needed for combustion to occur.
- A molecule is made up of two or more atoms of the same kind or different kinds, chemically joined together.
- The molecule of a compound consists of a fixed number of two or more different kinds of atoms chemically combined together.
- A chemical formula shows the number and kinds of atoms contained in each molecule.
- Ammonia is a compound of nitrogen and hydrogen. It is used for cleaning and to make fertilizers, explosives, and plastics.
- Chemical fertilizers contain mineral salts that can help plants to grow better.
- Used to excess, fertilizers can weaken or kill plants and pollute water.
- Most plastics are manufactured from oil.
- Plastics do not rot or corrode. They are light in weight, are good insulators, and can be made in many different colours.

Materials come in the three different forms that we call solid, liquid, and gas. These are known as the three states of matter. Every material is made up of tiny particles—either atoms or molecules. Which state a material is in (solid, liquid, or gas) depends on how strongly the particles stick together. How well the particles stick together depends on the material, the temperature, and the pressure.

Solids, liquids, and gases

We can recognise solids, liquids, and gases by their different properties:

Solids	Liquids	Gases
Have a definite volume	Have a definite volume	Have no definite volume—always fill the container they are in
Have a definite shape	Match the shape of their container	Become the same shape as their container
Particles packed closely	Particles are close together	Particles are far apart
Forces between particles are very strong	Forces between particles are quite strong	Forces between particles are very weak
Have a high density (are heavy for their size)	Have a medium density	Have a very low density
Are not easily squashed (or compressed)	Are not easily squashed (or compressed)	Are easily squashed (or compressed)
Expand slightly when heated	Expand quite a lot when heated	Expand greatly when heated
Do not flow	Flow easily	Flow easily and diffuse

Whether a material is a solid, liquid, or gas depends on the arrangement of the particles and their energy.

The particles in a solid have the least energy and they are packed close together. There are strong forces of attraction between the particles and they are held in fixed positions in a regular arrangement. The particles do not move from their positions, but they do vibrate to and fro. Solids keep a definite shape and volume and they cannot easily be compressed because the particles are already packed very close together.

How particles are arranged in a solid

There are some forces of attraction between the particles of a liquid. The particles also have more energy than those of a solid. Although the particles are close together, they are free to move past each other. The particles are constantly moving in all directions. Liquids do not keep a special shape and can spread out to form puddles. They flow and fill the bottom of a container, but they do keep the same volume. Liquids are quite dense because there are quite a lot of particles in a small volume. Liquids also do not compress easily.

How particles are arranged in a liquid

There are hardly any forces of attraction between the particles of a gas, so the particles are far apart and can move freely in all directions. The particles move so fast that they collide with each other and with the walls of their container. Gases do not keep a definite shape or volume and will always expand to fill any container. They can be compressed easily because there is a lot of space between the particles and they also have very low densities because there are not many particles in a large volume.

How particles are arranged in a gas

Physical changes

Physical changes alter a material without changing its chemical make-up. In other words, the particles in the material do not change, only the way they are arranged or their energy. Some of the words we use to describe a physical change include cutting, crushing, grinding, bending, breaking, melting, freezing, boiling, condensing, and dissolving.

A change of state is a physical change in which a substance changes from a solid to a liquid, or a liquid to a gas, or back again.

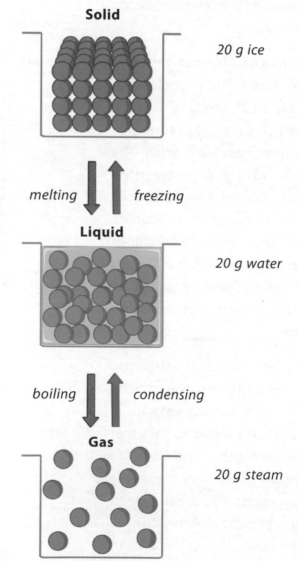

a. *When a solid is heated, its particles gain more energy and they vibrate more. This weakens the forces which hold the solid together and make it expand.*

b. *At a certain temperature, the particles have enough energy to break free from each other. This is called **melting** and the solid turns into a liquid.*

c. *When a liquid is heated, the particles get even more energy. The particles move faster and the bonds between them weaken and break.*

d. *At a certain temperature, the particles have enough energy to break their bonds. This is called boiling and the liquid turns into a gas.*

You will notice that the arrows in the diagram above point in both directions. This is because if you cool a gas, it will eventually condense and become a liquid. If you cool a liquid still further, it will eventually freeze and become a solid.

Reversible reactions

If water is cooled below 0°C it freezes to form ice. When the ice is warmed to a temperature above 0°C, it melts to form water. This is a **reversible reaction**. It can move in either direction, depending upon the conditions.

If blue crystals of copper sulphate are heated in a test-tube, water in the form of steam is given off. A white powder, called anhydrous copper sulphate is left in the tube. Anhydrous means 'without water'. If a few drops of water are added to the anhydrous copper sulphate, then the blue crystals are formed again.

copper sulphate crystals ⟷ anhydrous copper sulphate + water

The symbol ⟷ means that the change or reaction is reversible.

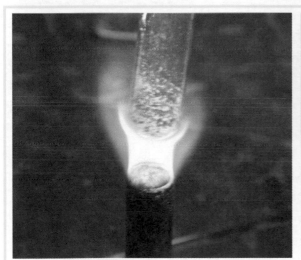

When heated, blue copper sulphate crystals turn to a white powder.

When water is added to anhydrous copper sulphate, it forms blue crystals again.

When the brown gas nitrogen dioxide is heated in a closed flask, its colour becomes lighter and lighter until, at 620°C, the gas is totally colourless. This is because it has broken down into nitric oxide and oxygen, both of which are colourless gases. When the flask is cooled, the nitric oxide and oxygen recombine and the flask is again filled with a brown gas.

nitrogen dioxide ⟷ nitric oxide + oxygen

Chemical changes

Physical changes are reversible. In a **chemical change**, one or more new substances are formed and it is not easy to reverse the process. When iron rusts, toast burns, or we boil an egg, new chemical compounds are formed. During photosynthesis and respiration new substances are formed. These are chemical changes, which are also known as **chemical reactions**.

In a chemical change or chemical reaction, four things happen:

- A new substance is produced which usually looks quite different from the substances you started with.

- Energy (usually heat energy) is given out or taken in during the reaction.

- The change may be impossible to reverse. In other words, most chemical changes are **non-reversible**.

- Although the atoms of each element combine in different ways, the same atoms that were there at the start are there at the end of the reaction. Because of this, the total mass stays the same.

Making bricks

The process of making bricks is a chemical reaction which has been used for thousands of years. To make bricks, sand, wet clay, and coal dust are mixed together and made into brick shapes. The brick shapes are left to dry for three days and then they are baked in an oven at 1200°C. The bricks are then left to cool, until they are ready to use. Right up the baking stage, the mixture is soft and can be cut or moulded. During the baking, the new hard material we call brick is produced. It is impossible to turn the brick back into the original ingredients after it has been baked.

Iron and sulphur

Sulphur is a yellow powder and iron filings are a greyish colour. A mixture of iron filings and sulphur can easily be separated using a magnet. The iron filings stick to the magnet, leaving the sulphur behind. Mixing iron and sulphur is a physical change since a new substance is not formed and you can mix the two together in any proportions.

Iron and sulphur

Mixing iron and sulphur

magnet

The chemical reaction between iron and sulphur

If iron filings and sulphur are gently heated, the yellow of the sulphur disappears and a dark grey substance is formed. This is iron sulphide. It is not possible to remove the iron from the iron sulphide with a magnet. Iron sulphide is a new substance and the heating has caused a chemical change to take place.

In the mixture, the particles of iron and sulphur remain separate and the numbers of each can vary. In the iron sulphide, particles of iron and sulphur are combined chemically in a fixed ratio.

We can summarise the reaction in a **word equation**:

iron + sulphur ⟶ iron sulphide

We can also write the reaction in symbols in a chemical equation:

$$Fe + S \longrightarrow FeS$$

iron filings

sulphur

heat

Mixture of sulphur and iron filings

The chemicals that you used at the start of the reaction (in this case iron and sulphur) are called **reactants**. The new substance(s) formed by the reaction (in this case iron sulphide) is called the **product(s)**.

Although you have to heat the iron and sulphur to start up this reaction, it gives out heat once it gets going. A reaction which gives out heat like this is called an **exothermic reaction**.

Magnesium and oxygen

Magnesium is a silvery grey metal. If you hold a piece of magnesium in a flame for a few seconds it will suddenly burn with a brilliant white light. Again, this is an exothermic reaction and the magnesium is combining with oxygen from the air to form a white powder. This new substance is called magnesium oxide

The word equation for this reaction is:

$$\text{magnesium} + \text{oxygen} \xrightarrow{\text{heat}} \text{magnesium oxide}$$

Or it can be written as a chemical equation:

$$2Mg + O_2 \longrightarrow 2MgO$$

The reaction when magnesium burns is very dramatic, as are many other exothermic reactions. Fireworks are designed by scientists who choose chemical substances, including sulphur and magnesium, and mix them in just the right amounts to produce light and sound energy, as well as heat energy.

Magnesium burns with a brilliant white flame.

Endothermic reactions

Some reactions take in heat while they are happening. These are called endothermic reactions. The process of photosynthesis involves taking in energy from sunlight, while cooking food is an example of an endothermic reaction. Heating lead oxide to produce the metal lead is another endothermic reaction.

Burning fuels

A fuel is a substance which can be burned to give heat or light. Fuels include wood, coal, oil, petrol, and natural gas (methane). Most fuels are hydrocarbons (compounds of hydrogen and carbon). When hydrocarbons burn, the main products are carbon dioxide and water, plus useful energy.

For example:

$$\text{methane} + \text{oxygen} \longrightarrow \text{carbon dioxide} + \text{water}$$

The chemical equation for this exothermic reaction is:

$$CH_4 + 2O_2 \longrightarrow CO_2 + 2H_2O$$

It is important to remember that three things are needed for burning or combustion to occur: fuel, heat, and oxygen.

Making ammonia

Ammonia is a very useful chemical substance. This strong-smelling, colourless gas, with the formula NH_3, is used in smelling salts to revive people when they have fainted. It is also used in cleaning fluids around the home, and in making some fertilizers, explosives, and plastics. Ammonia is produced by mixing the gases hydrogen and nitrogen under pressure. The nitrogen is obtained from liquid air, while the hydrogen is made by reacting the methane in natural gas with steam. Hot pellets of iron are also needed to make the nitrogen and hydrogen combine to form ammonia. The word equation for the reaction is:

$$\text{nitrogen} + \text{hydrogen} \xrightarrow{\text{hot iron}} \text{ammonia}$$

The hot iron does not take part in the reaction (it is not a reactant), but it needs to be there to make it happen. Substances which help a reaction along are called catalysts. At the end of the reaction, a catalyst has not been changed. It is exactly the same as it was at the beginning.

Ammonia and other fertilizers

Much of the ammonia produced every year is used to make fertilizers. Fertilizers containing nitrogen make plants grow better and produce lots of lush green leaves. If there is not enough nitrogen in the soil, plants become stunted and start to turn yellow. These plants do not produce high yields of crops.

The ammonia fertilizers are made by mixing ammonia gas with hot nitric acid. The solution is then sprayed into the top of a tower. The droplets fall into a rising current of cold air and form pellets. The ammonia gas, when changed into ammonium salts, provides crops with the nitrogen they need.

The chemical industry also makes huge quantities of fertilizers that contain phosphorus—another mineral that is essential, if plants are to grow healthily. The fertilizer called superphosphate is manufactured by treating natural phosphate rock with sulphuric acid.

Fertilizer being spread on a field

Dangers of fertilizers

Fertilizers can make crops grow better because they provide the mineral salts that plants need to grow healthily. They can improve the yield of crops—as long as they are used in the correct amounts. To test fertilizers, agricultural scientists grow two identical groups of plants and give fertilizer to one group. Then they compare the growth and yield of the two groups at the end of the growing season.

Too much fertilizer can make plants grow long and weak, so that they easily catch diseases and die. If the fertilizer builds up in the soil, it can stop the plants taking up water. Instead, water passes from the plant roots into the soil, causing the plants to wilt and eventually die. Heavy rain can also wash fertilizer into rivers. This leads to the rapid growth of water plants and a decrease in the amount of oxygen in the water. The plants die and so do the animals which depend upon the plants for food and oxygen. Huge numbers of bacteria use the dead plants and animals for food, while the amount of oxygen in the water decreases still further. This polluted water could finish up eventually in our drinking supplies.

OXFORD
UNIVERSITY PRESS

Margarine

You might not believe it, but the margarine you spread on your bread is made with the help of hydrogen, a colourless, odourless gas which can burn explosively. The basis of margarine is a vegetable oil, such as sunflower oil, palm oil, olive oil, rapeseed oil, or soya bean oil. To make margarine, the runny oil has to be turned into a solid fat. This is done by warming the oil to about 60°C and then bubbling hydrogen through it. This process is called hydrogenation. Nickel is used as a catalyst for the reaction to make it happen faster. The hydrogenation process raises the melting point of the oil, so that it is a solid rather than a liquid at room temperature. By controlling the amount of hydrogen bubbled into the oil, the margarine can be made as hard or as soft as is needed.

Plastics

We see plastics all around us—in the home, at school, at work, and in the street. There is no single material called 'plastic'. Scientists and engineers have created a whole series of plastics, each with a slightly different composition. These often have different uses, but most plastics have several similarities.

Plastics do not rot or corrode, like wood and metal. Most are good insulators—they block the movement of electricity and heat. Plastics are light in weight and can be made in many different colours.

Plastics are easy to mould. The word 'plastic' means soft. When a plastic is first heated it becomes soft and can be moulded into almost any shape.

Plastics do not rot or corrode, they are light in weight and they can be made in many colours.

Making plastics

All the materials we call plastics are made up of enormously long molecules. When you were young you might have joined loops of paper together to make a paper chain or beads to make a necklace. Scientists do a similar thing with plastics. They link together chemicals with small molecules to make a very long molecule called a **polymer**. This may contain tens of thousands of atoms. It is these long molecules that make plastics special.

There are some natural substances that have long molecules, including rubber, cotton, wool, and wood. But plastics are man-made materials manufactured from chemicals. In almost all plastics, the long chains that form the molecules are linked together by carbon atoms. Carbon is the only chemical element that behaves in this way. The main materials for making plastics are hydrocarbons from oil, coal, or gas. These are molecules composed of different numbers of carbon and hydrogen atoms. The finished plastics often include other atoms such as oxygen and nitrogen. The properties of plastics depend on the molecules of which they are made and the way in which these are linked.

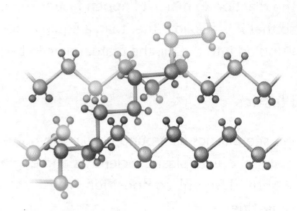

Whereas a sulphuric acid molecule contains only seven atoms, a polythene molecule may contain up to 50,000 atoms.

The world's first successful plastic was made in 1870 by an American inventor called John Hyatt. He was trying to produce an artificial ivory to use in making billiard balls. His invention was made from the cellulose in wood and was called celluloid. The plastics industry properly began in 1909, when an American chemist, Leo Baekeland, made Bakelite, a dark-coloured plastic, while trying to produce new types of varnish. Because of its excellent insulation properties, Bakelite can be used to insulate electrical equipment.

Polyethylene

One of the most useful hydrocarbons is the gas ethylene. Its chemical formula is written as C_2H_4. A molecule of ethylene is, therefore, composed of two atoms of carbon and four atoms of hydrogen.

Ethylene is obtained from the light oil called naphtha, which is produced when crude oil undergoes **fractional distillation**. Polyethylene is one of the world's most widely used plastics. As its name suggests, it is made up of many molecules of ethylene linked together. Polyethylene is a plastic material with a smooth, waxy texture. You probably know it better as polythene.

OXFORD
UNIVERSITY PRESS

Polyethylene was discovered in 1933. It is tough, waterproof, and a good electrical insulator. It therefore has a wide variety of uses, including making plastic bags and plastic sheets.

In 1953, a slightly different form of polyethylene was discovered. This is called high-density polyethylene. The two forms of polyethylene have the same composition, but in the high-density type the chains of molecules are much closer together. This type of plastic can withstand higher temperatures and is stronger. It is used in the home for washing-up bowls, buckets, and dustbins.

Polythene being manufactured

Polyvinylchloride

Polyvinylchloride, or PVC for short, is another common type of plastic. It is made by joining together the gases ethylene and chlorine. When these gases react they form a substance called ethylene dichloride. The ethylene dichloride is heated strongly to split up the molecules into vinyl chloride gas. These vinyl chloride molecules are then joined together to make the PVC polymer. A chemical is added to the polymer so that the PVC can be moulded. Otherwise it would change form when it was heated. The PVC can then be moulded into rigid colourless articles. To make flexible items, a substance called a plasticiser is added to the polymer. Colour may be added later.

Moulding machines turn the PVC into various shapes. Common uses are gutters and pipes for houses, and the insulation on electrical cables. PVC sheets are turned into plastic raincoats. Thin layers of PVC are used to make washable 'vinyl' wallpaper, while thicker layers are used to make soles for shoes and vinyl tiles.

Just a few of the items that are made from PVC

Questions

1. Name the only state of matter that can be easily compressed.

2. What happens to the speed at which particles move when they are heated?

3. Which two states of matter flow easily?

4. What is the arrangement of particles in a solid?

5. What is the opposite process to melting?

6. What will happen to the atoms or molecules of a substance when it:

    i. boils

    ii. melts

    iii. freezes

    iv. condenses?

7. How does the particle theory explain the properties of gases?

8. Explain the following terms and give three examples of each: i) element; ii) compound; iii) mixture; iv) physical change; v) chemical change.

9. What four things happen during a chemical change or chemical reaction?

10. Give three examples of a chemical change.

11. What is the difference between an endothermic reaction and an exothermic reaction? Give one example of each.

12. What is meant by the word 'fuel'? Give four examples of fuels.

13. What is a hydrocarbon?

14. What are the advantages and disadvantages of the use of fertilizers on crops and the soil?

15. What is hydrogen gas used for during the manufacture of margarine?

16. What are the advantages of the use of plastics instead of metals?

17. If you open a bottle of perfume in a room, the smell of the perfume soon spreads throughout the room. Explain why this is.

18. What is PVC? What are its properties and uses?

OXFORD
UNIVERSITY PRESS

Things to do

1. Devise an experiment to show how it is possible to distinguish between a physical and a chemical change.

2. Look around your home. How many examples of physical and chemical changes can you find? Make a list of each kind of change.

3. Devise an experiment to measure how much carbon dioxide gas there is in a given volume of fizzy drink. What volume of liquid will you use? How will you collect the gas? How will you measure the gas? What precautions will be necessary when you make your measurements?

Heat on the move

CHAPTER 10

Heat and temperature

This man is heating a steel horseshoe until it is red-hot, so that he can bend it to fit the horse's hoof.

Imagine yourself sitting in a bath of warm water. Which is hotter, the horseshoe or the bath full of hot water?

The answer is the horseshoe. Its **temperature** is about 650 to 750°C, whereas the water in the bath has a temperature of about 50°C.

Which contains more **heat**, the horseshoe or the bath of hot water? The answer this time is the hot water in the bath. The reason for the different answer is that temperature is a measure of how hot or cold something is and can be read on a **thermometer**. Heat is a form

BASIC FACTS

- Temperature tells us how hot or cold something is.
- We use a thermometer to measure temperature.
- We measure temperature in degrees Celsius (°C).
- Heat is a form of energy.
- Heat always travels from something hot to something cold, or from a hot part of something to a cold part.
- Everything is made up of particles (atoms and molecules) that are moving. When heat flows into something, it makes these particles move faster. When heat is lost, they slow down.
- If you feel cold it is because you are losing heat, not gaining cold.
- There are three ways that heat can travel: by conduction, convection, and radiation.
- Heat travels through solids by conduction.
- The best conductors of heat (or thermal conductors) are metals.
- Poor conductors of heat, like air, are called insulators.
- Heat is transferred in liquids and gases by convection.
- The movement of warm and cold gas or liquid produces a convection current.
- Radiation does not need particles to transfer heat energy from one place to another.
- Shiny, light surfaces reflect radiated heat.
- Matt black surfaces are good at emitting and absorbing radiated heat.

OXFORD
UNIVERSITY PRESS

of energy, and although the bath water is cooler than the red-hot horseshoe, it takes much more energy from the gas or electricity, or from a fire or furnace, to heat a whole bath full of water to 50°C. You could also think of it another way. If you had a bath full of cold water and you plunged a red-hot horseshoe into the water, the temperature of the water would only rise by a degree or so because there is so much of it to heat up.

Heat on the move

As you already know, everything is made up of particles (such as atoms or molecules) which are constantly on the move. When something is hot, its particles vibrate or move faster than when it is cold. In the example above, there are more particles in the bath of water than there are in the horseshoe because the water weighs much more than the horseshoe. The water therefore contains more energy in its moving particles than the horseshoe. But the horseshoe is at a higher temperature because the average energy of its particles is greater than that of the water.

If you leave a hot drink and an ice cube to stand in the same room for a little while, the drink cools down but the ice cube warms up. Eventually, the drink and the water from the melting ice cube will both be at the same temperature. This always happens. Objects that are warmer than their surroundings lose heat; objects that are cooler than their surroundings gain heat.

The energy given out or gained as heat can travel in three ways:

Conduction

If you put a metal spoon in a very hot drink, the handle of the spoon gets hot very quickly. What happens is this. When the bowl of the spoon is heated, the particles at that end of the spoon vibrate faster. This makes nearby particles vibrate more and so, gradually heat energy is passed along the handle of the spoon. Scientists say that the heat is travelling by **conduction**

In a similar way, the heat passes quickly from a flame or hotplate through a metal saucepan to heat the contents. Copper is an especially good conductor and expensive saucepans sometimes have copper bottoms to quickly conduct heat to the food inside the saucepan.

Metals are the best conductors of heat. This is because their particles are packed closely together and so the vibrations are passed on very quickly. Poor conductors of heat are called **insulators**

Good conductors of heat	Insulators (poor conductors of heat)
metals, especially:	water
copper	glass
aluminium	plastic
silver	wood
	cork
	paper
	cloth
	air
	materials with air trapped in them such as:
	wool
	plastic foam
	polystyrene
	fibreglass
	feathers

Notice that all the heat insulators are non-metals. They do not allow heat to flow easily through them. If you stir a cup of hot drink with a plastic spoon, the handle of the spoon will not get hot. Saucepans often have wooden or plastic handles. This stops the handle from getting too hot and burning your hands while the pan is being heated.

Most saucepans have a plastic or wooden handle to prevent the heat travelling to your hands.

Air is a particularly good heat insulator. Some of the best insulating materials, such as fur and feathers, trap tiny pockets of air. As we saw on page 58, the hairs on a polar bear are actually tiny hollow tubes which trap air. Quilts and ski jackets keep us warm because they are made from a soft, padded material which traps lots of air between the fibres.

In cold weather a bird fluffs out its feathers to trap a layer of air around its body.

Whether something is a conductor or insulator of heat affects how it feels when we touch it. If you hold the wooden handle of a spade and then touch the metal blade, the metal feels colder even though both the handle and the blade are at the same temperature. The reason for the difference is that your fingertips are warmer than the metal and heat flows easily from your fingers into the metal, making them feel cold. Wood is a poor conductor of heat. Heat does not flow easily from your fingers into the wood and so, your fingers stay warm.

Convection

If air is heated, it expands (its particles spread out) and it rises. Cooler, 'heavier' air moves in to take its place. If you place your hand a little way above a hot radiator, you can feel the warm air rising. If you tie some strips of tissue paper around the end of a short stick and hold it above the radiator, the rising air currents will make the strips of paper move. As it moves along the ceiling, the warm air cools and sinks, and the cold air moves across the floor towards the hot radiator. This circulating flow of air is called a **convection current** and the radiator warms the room by **convection**.

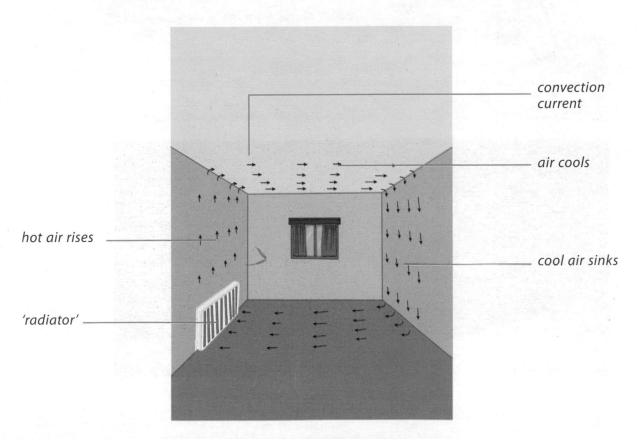

convection current

air cools

hot air rises

cool air sinks

'radiator'

Most rooms are heated by convection currents.

Convection currents and the weather

Convection currents also have a part to play in the weather, as wind is air on the move. During the day, the Sun warms up the land more quickly than the sea. The warm air above the land rises. This is because it is 'lighter' or less dense than cold air. Cooler, 'heavier' air from over the sea moves in to take its place. This sets up a convection current so that during the day cool breezes blow in from the sea.

At night, the opposite occurs. The land cools down more quickly than the sea. The air over the sea is warmer and so it rises. This produces a land breeze, caused by the cooler air over the land moving out to sea.

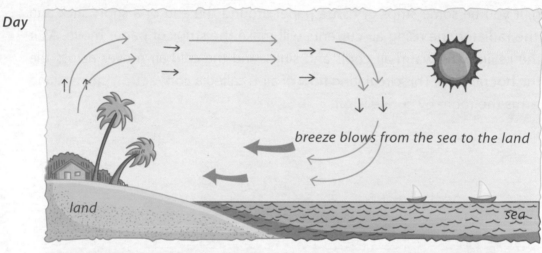

How land and sea breezes form

The wind systems of the world are mainly due to currents of hot air rising over the equator, and cooler air from above the poles moving in to take their place.

Using convection currents in the air

Some birds make use of convection currents when they fly. Eagles, storks, and pelicans will use the rising convection currents called thermals, to enable them to soar with very little effort when they are **migrating**. Many eagles, hawks, buzzards, and vultures use thermals when they soar in search of food. Soaring birds always have large and broad wings.

Gliders use thermals to allow them to stay in the air. An aeroplane or a winch tows the glider into the air. The glider pilot then uses thermals to help the aircraft to rise and stay up in the air.

Eagles use thermals to allow them to soar effortlessly when they are hunting or migrating.

Convection currents in liquids

Convection currents also occur in water and other liquids. The water in a pan over a fire, gas ring, or hotplate is heated all through, even though the heat is only applied at the bottom. This is because water circulates in the pan because of convection. The water near to the base of the pan becomes warm and expands. This water is less dense ('lighter') and so it rises. Cooler water sinks to take its place. This water movements continues until all the water is at the same temperature.

Heating and cooling with convection currents

The domestic hot-water system is another example of the use of convection currents. In a simple system, water that has been heated in a boiler rises into a storage tank, while cold water from a tank in the roof flows down to the boiler to be heated. The hot-water taps are fed by gravity from the storage tank.

A central heating system works on a similar principle. The only difference is that when a number of radiators have to be fed with hot water, a pump often helps the natural convection currents to circulate the hot water.

The water pump in a car engine also helps the natural convection currents to circulate water more quickly. The water is heated when it passes through channels in the cylinder block, thus keeping the engine cool. The hot water is then pumped through the car radiator where it gives up its heat to the air outside.

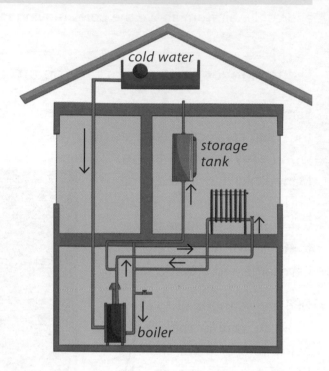

How convection currents circulate hot water in a house

Ocean currents

The waters of the oceans and seas are constantly moving. As well as the waves and tides, ocean water flows around the Earth in great rivers called currents. Currents on the ocean surface are driven by the winds. They travel in more or less the same direction that the wind blows most often.

There are also currents that flow from the surface down towards the sea floor and down along the ocean bottom. The currents flow because some parts of the

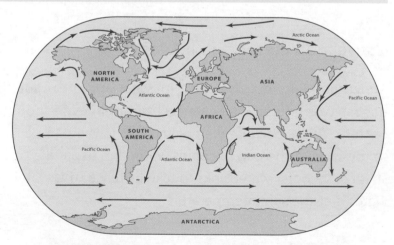

A map showing some of the main ocean currents

oceans are colder than others, while others are saltier than others. Cold, salty water is denser than warm, fresh water, so it sinks. Once the water warms up or gets diluted with less salty water, it will rise back to the surface.

Radiation

The Earth is warmed by heat energy coming to it from the Sun, which is about 150 million km away. The heat cannot travel from the Sun to the Earth by conduction or convection. This is because the space between the Sun and the Earth is almost a **vacuum**—a perfectly empty space. Conduction and convection can only take place where there is matter. You can see the sunlight, but you cannot see the Sun's heat, even though you can feel it on your skin. The Sun's heat energy that travels through empty space is called **radiant heat** or **infrared radiation**.

An **eclipse** of the Sun occurs when the Moon passes directly between the Earth and the Sun. When that happens, the heat and light of the Sun are cut off at the same moment. This shows that heat and light travel at the same speed. Radio waves, which carry our radio and television programmes, also travel at this speed and they too can travel through a vacuum. In fact, radiant heat, light, and radio waves are all forms of what is called **electromagnetic radiation**. They differ only in the rate at which their waves pass by.

Reflecting or absorbing radiation

Just as light can be reflected or absorbed by objects and materials, so too can radiant heat. White or shiny metal surfaces are best at reflecting heat, which means they are poor at absorbing it. In hot, sunny countries, buildings are often painted white, so that they absorb as little of the Sun's radiation as possible. Kettles and saucepans are usually made silvery or white so that they lose heat slowly. On a hot, sunny day it is a good idea to wear white or light colours to keep cool.

These white painted houses reflect the Sun's heat and so keep the insides cool.

Dull black surfaces are best at absorbing heat. They are also best at giving off radiation. In hot, sunny weather, the inside of a black-coloured car is much hotter than the inside of a silver or white car of the same make and model.

Emitting radiation

A hot object gives out, or emits, heat energy as radiation. If you put your hand near something hot (without touching it!) you can feel the heat on your skin. Everything gives off some heat energy as radiation. Even your body emits heat energy. The hotter an object is, the more heat energy it radiates. Infrared waves are produced by the vibrating particles of whatever is giving out the heat. The higher the temperature of the object, the more rapidly its particles vibrate and the greater the frequency of the waves.

When the heating element of an electric cooker is switched on, it first gives out only infrared radiation, or black heat as it is sometimes called. You can tell that the heating element is warming up if you hold your hand just above it—but do not touch it! Then, as the heating element gets hotter, its particles start to vibrate more vigorously and it gives out the familiar red glow. If it were possible to heat it even more, it would give out a white light (a mixture of all colours), and then finally melt.

Radiation and the greenhouse effect

Some infrared radiation from the Sun can pass through glass because the Sun is very hot and it emits high-energy radiation. This is how infrared radiation passes through the glass of a greenhouse. The plants and soil inside the greenhouse are not so hot. They radiate infrared rays of lower energy that cannot pass through the glass. The energy is trapped and the greenhouse warms up.

In a similar way, the Earth's atmosphere acts like the glass in a greenhouse, trapping energy from the Sun. Without this **greenhouse effect**, the Earth would be too cold for life to exist. But polluting gases, such as carbon dioxide from the burning of fossil fuels in, for example, power stations, factories, and motor vehicles, can increase the effect. This extra warming is known as **global warming**. It is altering the distribution of wind and moisture around the world and causing extreme weather conditions and problems for plants and animals, including humans.

Infra-red radiation passes through the glass of this greenhouse to heat the inside.

Fires, irons, and thermal imaging cameras

Like the heating element on an electric cooking range, an electric fire also gets hot enough to glow red. Incidentally, you may have noticed that the reflector behind the heating element of the fire is made of shiny curved metal, so that it reflects the heat into the room. An electric iron, used for ironing clothes, is not hot enough to radiate visible light, but it does still give off infrared rays.

The vacuum flask

The **vacuum flask**, or Thermos, was invented by a Scottish scientist, James Dewar (1842-1923). It keeps hot drinks hot and cold drinks cold by stopping the movement of heat. The flask consists of a glass bottle with double walls. There is a vacuum between these glass walls which stops the conduction and convection of heat. Radiation of heat is prevented because the walls of the glass have a silver coating. The stopper is made of a good insulating material such as cork, or hollow plastic.

Modern vacuum flasks often have a double-sided metal bottle instead of a glass one because metal is stronger.

Thermographs

Thermal imaging cameras use special film to take photographs with infrared rays. These photographs are called thermographs. In a thermograph, different colours show which parts of an object are warm and which are cool.

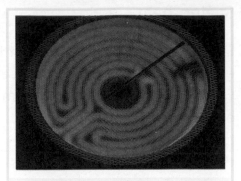

The heating element of a hot plate glows red as it emits radiation.

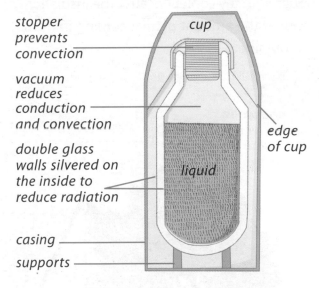

stopper prevents convection

cup

vacuum reduces conduction and convection

double glass walls silvered on the inside to reduce radiation

edge of cup

liquid

casing

supports

Inside a vacuum flask

Thermographs are used in medicine because diseased tissue is often warmer than healthy tissue. By using a thermal imaging camera, cancers deep inside the body can be made to show up. Thermographs can also show where and how heat is being lost from a building. Electricity supply companies use thermal imaging cameras to detect overheating wiring and parts of power lines. Fire fighters use thermal imaging to see through smoke to find trapped people and detect where a fire started.

Fire fighters use thermal imaging camera to locate people trapped in a burning building.

Saving heat

In cold climates, a great deal of heat can escape from a building. This is an expensive waste of fuel, as well as being harmful to the environment. Over one-third of the heat is lost through the walls, a quarter is lost through the roof, while the rest escapes through the doors, windows, and floors. To prevent these heat losses, buildings need to be well insulated.

In places with a hot climate, a well-insulated house will stay cooler because the insulation reduces the amount of heat coming in from the outside.

This thermograph shows how heat is being lost from the different parts of a house in a cold climate.

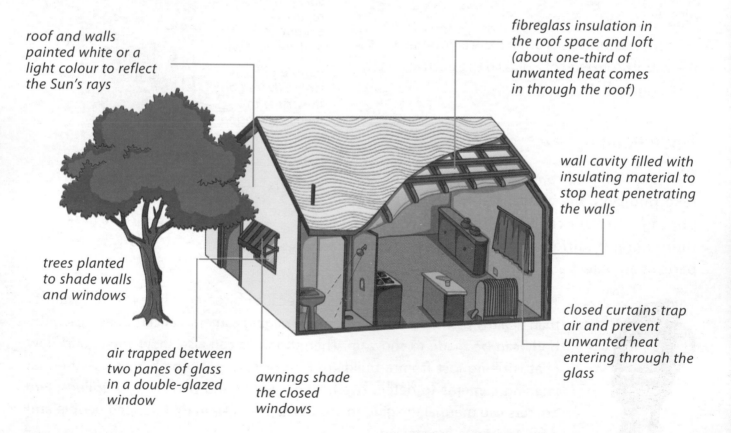

roof and walls painted white or a light colour to reflect the Sun's rays

fibreglass insulation in the roof space and loft (about one-third of unwanted heat comes in through the roof)

wall cavity filled with insulating material to stop heat penetrating the walls

trees planted to shade walls and windows

closed curtains trap air and prevent unwanted heat entering through the glass

air trapped between two panes of glass in a double-glazed window

awnings shade the closed windows

How a house can be kept cool

OXFORD
UNIVERSITY PRESS

Questions

1. Which unit is used to measure temperature?

2. Which has more heat, a full bath at 50°C or a cup of tea at a temperature of 85°C?

3. Why does a jacket potato cook much more quickly if you put a metal skewer through it?

4. Why does a quilt keep you less warm if it has been flattened?

5. Explain why birds often fluff out their feathers in cold weather.

6. Air is a mixture of gases and its particles are spread out. Explain why this makes air a bad conductor of heat.

7. Name and define three methods of heat transfer and give an example of each.

8. Explain why energy from the Sun cannot reach us by conduction or convection.

9. If you get out of bed in the morning onto a tiled floor, your feet feel cold. But if you walk on a carpet in your bare feet, it feels warm. Why is there this difference?

10. Why do the so-called radiators which are part of a central heating system have the wrong name? Explain your answer.

11. If you found yourself in a smoke-filled room, why would it be sensible to stay as close to the floor as possible?

12. What is the main disadvantage of using metal instead of glass in a vacuum flask?

13. What are thermographs? Describe their uses.

14. How can we make our houses cool in summer and warm in winter?

1. Draw a labelled diagram showing how convection currents heat the water inside an electric kettle.

2. A refrigerator uses convection to keep food cool. The cooling element is placed near the top of the refrigerator. Explain with the aid of a diagram how the air inside the refrigerator circulates until the whole of the inside is cool.

3. Devise an experiment, using a balloon, to show what happens when a gas or a mixture of gases is heated. Draw a labelled diagram of the apparatus you would use. Describe what you expect would happen if you carried out the experiment.

Dispersion of light

CHAPTER 11

BASIC FACTS

- Unlike sound, light can pass through a vacuum.
- When light travels from one transparent material to another, it bends or refracts.
- When light goes from a less dense transparent material to a denser transparent material, it bends towards the normal.
- When light goes from a dense transparent material to a less dense transparent material, it bends away from the normal.
- Lenses are made of transparent material with one or more curved surfaces. They are used for refracting light.
- Light can be made to reflect internally from the surface of a material. This happens when the angle of incidence is equal to, or greater than, the critical angle.

- White light is not just a single colour.
- The spreading or dispersal of white light gives a spectrum.
- A spectrum is a band of colours formed by the separation of white light into its component colours.
- Rainbows form when sunlight is dispersed through raindrops.
- The primary colours of light are red, green, and blue.
- Mixing red, green, and blue lights produces white light.
- Mixing coloured lights produces colours by addition.
- Coloured objects reflect light only of their particular colour.
- A filter only allows light of one particular colour to go through—the colour of the filter itself.
- Objects seem to change colour in coloured light.
- The cone cells in the retina at the back of each eye are sensitive to colours.

Light is a form of energy we can see. Like sound, light travels as a wave, but unlike sound light does not depend on vibrations and does not need a material to travel through. Sunlight travels through a completely empty space to reach the Earth. A few things give off their own light, including the Sun and other stars, light bulbs, candles, and fires. These are called **luminous** objects. We see everything because the light is reflected from it into our eyes.

Light always travels in straight lines.

Straight lines

Light always travels in straight lines at very high speeds. It travels at different speeds through different substances. Light travels fastest through a vacuum, such as through space. Its speed then is about 300,000 kilometres per second. Nothing can travel faster than this. Light can only go through material that are **transparent**. We cannot see through a brick wall because it is **opaque**. Some things, like frosted bathroom windows, are **translucent** which means they let some light through, but not enough to see by.

Refraction

Light will not travel through an opaque material, but it will go through anything transparent, such as air, glass, or water. When light travels from one transparent material to another, it bends or **refracts**

You can see the effects of refraction if you look at a tank of fish. The fish, and the back of the tank, seem much closer than they really are. When you go to a swimming pool, the water does not look as deep as it really is. If you put one end of a straight stick in water, it appears to bend where it enters the water.

What is happening in the examples above is that a change in the speed of light has made it change direction. As light enters water or any other dense transparent material it slows down. Light travelling from air to water slows down from just under 300,000 kilometres per second to about 250,000 kilometers per second.

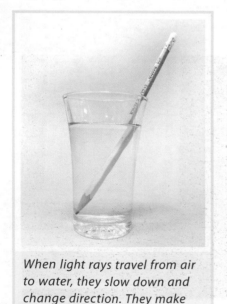

When light rays travel from air to water, they slow down and change direction. They make the pencil look bent where it enters the water.

light ray

air

glass

angle of refraction

angle of incidence

normal

refracted ray

normal

light ray emerging

How light rays are bent or refracted by a block of glass

If the light enters glass, it slows down even further to between about 150,000 and 200,000 kilometres metres per second.

Refraction is the name given to this change in the speed of light. A ray of light is always refracted in a definite direction. The Law of Refraction of light states that as light goes into a denser material, such as from air to glass, it bends towards the normal. As light passes from a dense material, such as glass or water, into a less dense material, such as air, it is bent away from the normal. The normal is a line drawn at right angles to the surface.

If you pass a beam of light through a rectangular block of glass, the ray of light is refracted as it enters and as it leaves the block. The ray that emerges from the block is parallel to the ray that entered the block.

Refractive index

Not all materials bend light to the same extent. Some materials refract light more than others. Because refraction occurs where two materials meet, then two materials must be involved each time refraction occurs. Each pair of materials is given a label or index that shows how much the pair refracts light. This index is called the refractive index (RI). The higher the refractive index, the more light will be refracted.

$$\text{refractive index} = \frac{\text{speed of light in a vacuum}}{\text{speed of light in material}}$$

The refractive index of soda-lime glass is 1.5.

The speed of light in this type of glass is

$$1.5 = \frac{300,000 \text{ km/s}}{\text{speed in glass}}$$

$$\text{speed in glass} = \frac{300,000 \text{ km/s}}{1.5} = 200,000 \text{ km/s}$$

This equation shows us that, in soda-lime glass, light travels at roughly two-thirds of the speed of light in a vacuum. Water has a refractive index of 1.33. This means that in water light travels at three-quarters of the speed it would travel in a vacuum.

The table below shows some examples of the refractive index values for pairs of materials:

Air to material	Material	Material to air
1.36	alcohol	0.73
1.66	calcite	0.60
1.51	crown glass	0.66
2.42	diamond	0.41
1.61	flint glass	0.62
1.31	ice	0.76
1.49	perspex	0.67
1.59	polystyrene	0.63
1.47	pyrex	0.68
1.54	quartz	0.65
4.01	silicon	0.25
1.50	soda-lime glass	0.66
1.33	water	0.75

If you see it said that, for example, 'water has a refractive index of 1.33', you should always assume that the other material is air and that light is travelling from the air into the water. If the light was travelling from water to air, then the refractive index would be 0.75.

Mirages

When light bends, it tricks our eyes into seeing things in the wrong place. A **mirage** is caused by the refraction of light in the atmosphere. Light travels more quickly through the warmer air near the ground than it does through the cooler air above. As a result, light is refracted so that its rays are bent up and come to our eyes from a different place from where they started. We see a false image of a distant object. Mirages are common in deserts where the

A mirage of a pool of water in a hot, dry desert. It is really light from the sky being bent upwards by a layer of hot air close to the ground.

OXFORD
UNIVERSITY PRESS

air near the ground is very hot. A mirage can make it look as if there is a lake ahead, when really it is an image of the sky. You may also see mirages along a hot road, when the road in the distance seems to be shimmering wet.

Total internal reflection

Sometimes when light rays enter a denser substance, they never leave. They are reflected backwards and forwards inside it. This is called **total internal reflection**.

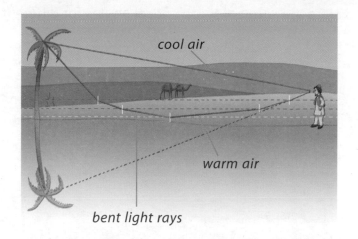

How a mirage is formed

If a light ray strikes a transparent material and the angle of incidence is zero, then there is no refraction. Once it is in the material, the light ray continues in a straight line. When it meets the next boundary and the angle of incidence is also zero, there will be no noticeable refraction or bending of the light ray. For the refraction or bending to be noticeable, the angle of incidence of the light ray must be greater than zero.

In order for a light ray travelling inside a material to get out, it must leave the far edge of the material. When the light ray strikes this edge it will be refracted for a second time. The angle at which it strikes this second boundary is important. If this angle of incidence is too large, the light will not escape. It will not be refracted. Instead it will be reflected back into the material because the second surface acts like a mirror. The angle of incidence at which all refraction stops is known as the **critical angle** for the material. Each material has its own special value for this angle. The critical angle of glass is 41°. If light strikes the inside surface of a block of glass at this angle or a larger angle, it will be totally internally reflected. Refraction will not occur.

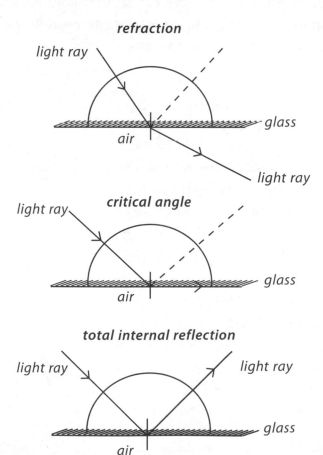

Here are some of these critical angles for different materials:

Material	Critical angle
crown glass	41°
diamond	24°
ice	49°
Perspex	42°
water	48°

The sparkle of diamonds is due to the total internal reflection of light rays.

Diamond has a critical angle of 24°. This means that if a light ray travelling inside a diamond strikes an inside surface at an angle of 24° or *more*, it will not be refracted and escape. Instead the light ray will be reflected internally. Use is made of this fact when diamonds are cut and polished. The faces are cut so that light is totally internally reflected and the diamond sparkles. For water to show total internal reflection, light rays have to strike the inside surface at an angle of more than 48°.

Using internal reflection

As well as being able to make diamonds sparkle, we can use total internal reflection in several other ways. Because of total internal reflection, a **prism** can be made to act like a perfect mirror. It has the advantage that there is no need for a reflective coating which can corrode or peel away over time. Such prisms are used in expensive periscopes and also in some binoculars and telescopes.

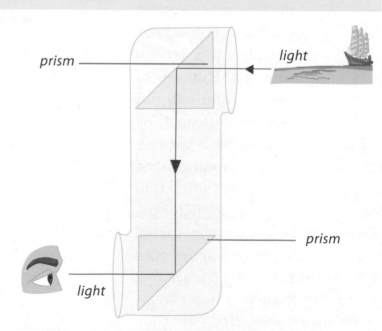

prism

light

light

prism

This periscope uses total internal reflection inside triangular prisms.

OXFORD
UNIVERSITY PRESS

Optical fibres are very thin flexible glass rods. Light reflects internally the whole length of the fibre because light always hits the sides of the fibre at an angle greater than the critical angle. This means that all the light is reflected and little energy is lost. The light emerges from the end of the fibre almost as bright as it went in. Bundles of optical fibres, fixed to a special camera or eyepiece, are used to see inside machinery and even inside the human body. Optical fibres can also carry coded signals as pulses of light from a laser. These can be changed into electrical signals at the receiving end. Nowadays many of our telephone calls are sent down bundles of optical fibres which can carry several thousand messages at once.

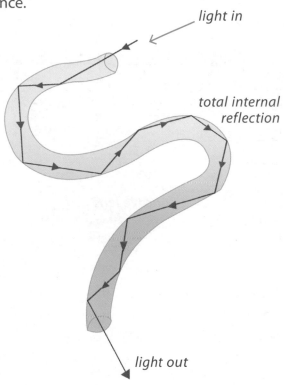

light in

total internal reflection

light out

An optical fibre highly magnified

Fibre optics allow surgeons to look inside the human body.

Lenses

Lenses come in various shapes and sizes. The two most common types are convex and concave lenses. If you look at something close up with a convex lens, you see a magnified image. If you look through a concave lens, you can see a lot of your surroundings, but the image appears smaller than normal. A distant object appears upside down.

Lenses work because light is refracted or bent when it passes from air into glass. A convex lens can converge (bring together) parallel light rays after they have passed through the lens. A concave lens diverges (spreads out) parallel rays of light so that they appear to come from a focal point on the other side of the lens.

Each of our eyes has a natural lens which can change shape so that it can focus on near and distant objects. You are using those lenses to read this page now. Microscopes, telescopes, projectors, cameras, and magnifying glasses make use of convex lenses. Spectacles and contact lenses may use either convex or concave lenses, depending on what is wrong with the person's eyesight. Concave lenses are used in spectacles and contact lenses for short-sighted people, who cannot see things clearly that are a long way away. Convex lenses are used in spectacles and contact lenses for long-sighted people who cannot see things clearly that are close to their eyes.

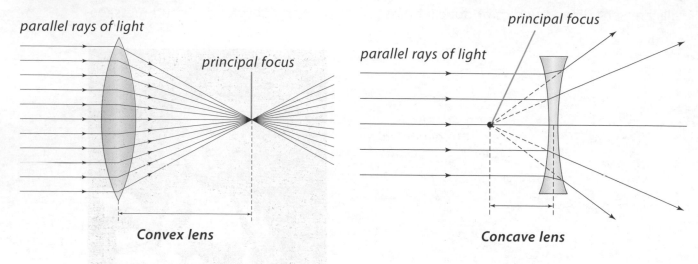

Convex lens

Concave lens

Prisms and refraction

When a beam of white light is refracted, something else happens. The light is dispersed, or spread out, into different colours. It may surprise you to learn that white light is actually a mixture of colours! You can see this dispersion if you shine a beam of white light through a triangular-shaped **prism**

What happens is that the prism refracts the different wavelengths of light by different amounts. It disperses or spreads them out into a rainbow spread of colour called a **spectrum**, so that they can be seen. Red light is refracted least and appears at the top of the spectrum, while violet light is refracted most and appears at the bottom of the spectrum. Although you cannot see them, infra-red and ultra-violet rays could be present at the top and bottom of the spectrum that your eyes can actually see.

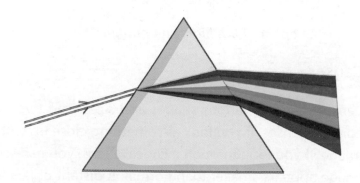

When white light passes through a prism it changes direction and also splits up, or disperses into all the colours of the spectrum.

Rainbows

You can only see a rainbow when the Sun is shining behind you and it is raining in front of you. Rainbows form when sunlight shines through millions of raindrops. When sunlight passes through one of these raindrops, the raindrop acts like a tiny prism. Each ray of light is bent as it enters the raindrop, and as it leaves it. It is also reflected off the inside of the raindrop. The light spreads out and is split into seven colours. The drawing below shows this happening to just one raindrop.

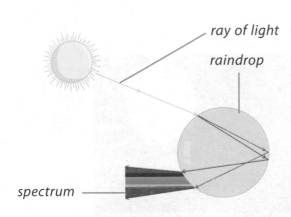

How sunlight is split by a raindrop

A rainbow is really a spectrum in the sky. The colours are, from the outside inwards, are red, orange, yellow, green, blue, indigo, and violet.

When this happens in millions of raindrops, the effect is to give a bow with the reddish colours on top (the outside of the rainbow) and the bluish colours on the bottom (the inside of the rainbow). All rainbows are actually part of a circle, but you can usually see only part of it as the Earth is in the way. Sometimes you can see a complete circle from an aircraft.

Mixing coloured lights

The first person to show that white light is a mixture of light of different colours was a young English scientist—Isaac Newton in about 1666. He bought a triangular prism at a country fair. When he got home, he shone a narrow beam of white light through the prism onto a screen. He found that the light was split up into a rainbow-coloured band. He had produced a spectrum.

It was also Newton who showed that it was possible to combine all the coloured lights in a spectrum and form white light again. He did this by using two triangular prisms, one to split up white light and the other, placed upside down, to join the colours together again.

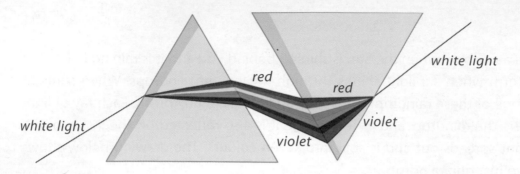

Using two prisms to split up and recombine the colours of the spectrum to form white light

Newton also discovered that the colours of the spectrum could be joined together another way. He did this with what we now call Newton's colour disc. This is a circular disc divided up into sections, each of which is one of the colours of the spectrum. When the disc is spun rapidly, the colours are mixed by our eyes and the disc looks white.

Newton's colour disc
Left: when still   Right: when turned rapidly

Primary coloured lights

It is not necessary to mix together lights of all the colours of the spectrum to make white light again. You can do it with just three colours—red, green, and blue. Red, green, and blue are known as the **primary colours** of light. If red, green, and blue lights are mixed together, we see them as white light.

Primary colours mix together to give all the other colours. Where two primary coloured lights overlap, they produce a **secondary colour**. Red and blue make magenta. Red and green make yellow. Green and blue make cyan.

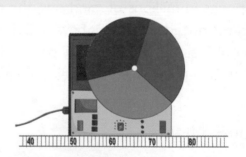

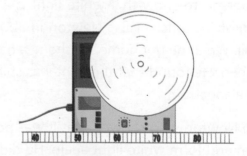

The three primary colours of light can be mixed in different combinations to make any other colour.

Seeing colours

The sensitive screen at the back of the eye is called the **retina**. It has two types of cells called **rods** and **cones** You have about 120 million rod cells and 6 million cone cells in each eye. The rods are mainly around the edge of the retina and are sensitive to dim light. The cones are sensitive to bright light and to red, green, and blue light. Our brain makes out all the other colours by combining the signals from these cells. Yellow light, for example, stimulates the red and green cells, but not the blue ones. The brain has learnt to recognise this combined signal as coming from yellow light.

Some of the colours we see are not part of the spectrum at all. For example, there is no wavelength of light for the colour brown. The brain invents such colours mixing signals from the eye.

Some people's cones do not work properly and they cannot see colours accurately. A few people are colour blind, not being able to see some colours, e.g. red, blue, etc. Much more common, especially among men, is a form of colour blindness where reds and greens get mixed up.

If your colour vision is normal, you will be able to see number 3.

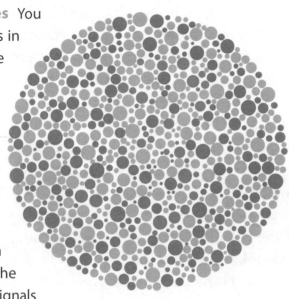

Colours on screen

When you watch a television screen or look at a computer, you are seeing the effects of adding colours together. A television screen or computer screen is made up of tiny red, green, and blue dots close together. We see a whole variety of colours because these dots are made to shine with different brightnesses. A dress is made to look yellow on the screen by making the red and green dots shine much more brightly than the blue ones. This produces exactly the same signal to the brain as yellow light and so the brain is 'tricked' into seeing a yellow dress.

The picture on a television screen is made up of tiny dots of just three colours—red, green, and blue.

Colour subtraction

Most of the objects we see do not produce light themselves. Instead they reflect light into our eyes. They are coloured by a process called colour subtraction. They subtract, or absorb, some of the colours of the spectrum, but not others. A leaf, for example, looks green because it absorbs nearly all the colours in sunlight, except one—green. A red car reflects red light, and absorbs the other colours of the spectrum. On the other hand, an object or material that reflects all of the colours equally well, such as snow, will look white. A blackboard looks black because it is hardly reflecting any light at all.

Red light reflected

The car appears red in white light because it reflects red light and absorbs all the other colours of the spectrum.

Filters

A filter is a coloured film that fits over a lamp or camera lens to change the colour of the light passing through it. But the filter does not actually colour the light, in the way that you might use a dye to colour a fabric. Instead the filter works rather like a tea-strainer, removing unwanted tea leaves. A colour filter removes unwanted light. It absorbs all the other colours in the white light. As a result, the light that has come through a filter is always dimmer. A red filter stops blue and green and allows only red light to pass through. A blue filter stops everything except blue light. A green filter, for example, absorbs the red and blue lights and allows the green·to pass through. A magenta filter absorbs green light and allows red and blue to pass through.

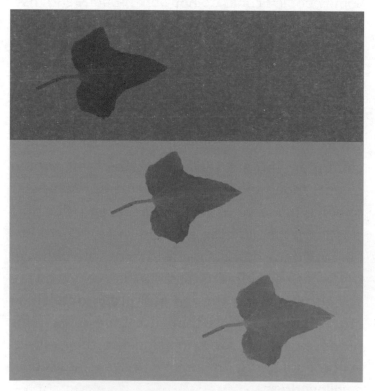

The appearance of a green leaf when different coloured filters are used

Mixing coloured pigments

It is also possible to make any colour paint or ink if you have only three colours to start with. You need to start with the colours, red, blue, and yellow. These are the three primary colours of paints and pigments.

Green, orange, and magenta are known as the **secondary colours** of paints and pigments.

Every coloured photograph and drawing you see is produced from just four coloured inks—magenta, cyan, yellow, and black. Mixing these colours together in different proportions produces all the different colours you can see. When a book or magazine is prepared for printing, the colour images are scanned to separate the four colours photographically. A printing plate is then prepared for each colour. When the pages are printed, each printing plate adds its own separate colour, so that the final picture has the same colours as the original photograph or drawing.

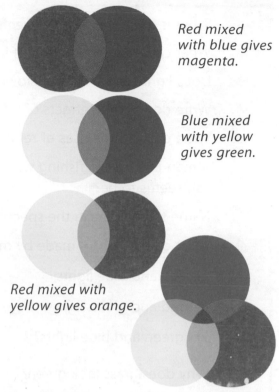

Red mixed with blue gives magenta.

Blue mixed with yellow gives green.

Red mixed with yellow gives orange.

Red, yellow, and blue together give black.

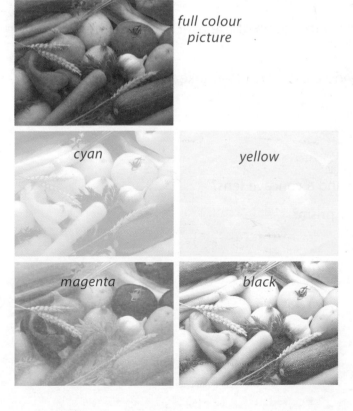

full colour picture

cyan

yellow

magenta

black

Colour printing uses only four coloured inks—cyan, yellow, magenta, and black.

1. What is the difference between reflection and refraction?

2. What causes the refraction of light?

3. Does light travel faster or slower in water than in air? Why is this?

4. Write down three effects of refraction.

5. Write down three uses of refraction.

6. A man in a boat is fishing with a spear. Why does not he aim his spear where the fish seems to be?

7. Name the colours in the spectrum of white light.

8. What colour light is made by mixing:

    i.   red and blue lights;

    ii. red and green lights;

    iii. green and blue lights?

9. Why does grass look green?

10. How does a colour filter work?

11. What would you see if you passed white light through a blue filter and then a red filter?

12. What is the name of the two kinds of cells in the retina of the eye? What are they each sensitive to?

13. When they are shopping for clothes, why do customers often take items to the window to look at them?

14. What is optic fibre? Describe how it is used.

15. Explain why we see rainbows?

16. What is the difference between a convex and a concave lens?

17. What would you see if a light ray falls on a prism?

Things to do

1. Place a ruler in a glass of water. Look along the length of the ruler into the water. Does the ruler still seem straight?

2. Place a coin at the bottom of a tin can or container made of opaque plastic. Move your eyes away from the can or container until the coin is just out of sight. Keep your eyes in this position, while a friend slowly and carefully pours water into the can or container. What happens? Explain you results.

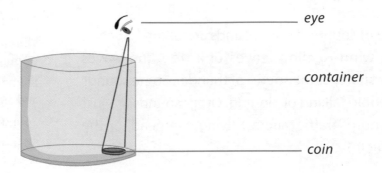

eye

container

coin

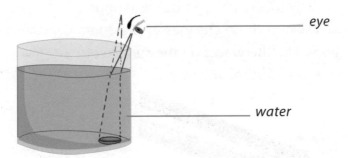

eye

water

Sound waves

CHAPTER 12

Sounds all around

Our world is full of sounds. Some sounds are natural, such as bird song, the wind rustling leaves of a tree, the waves breaking on the shore, or the sound of thunder. Some sounds are made by people talking or singing. Other sounds are just noise—the sound of traffic, aircraft flying overhead, or the machines in a factory.

Whatever kind of sound you hear, it is caused by something moving—the slamming of a door, footsteps, the wind moving the leaves or branches of a tree. Every movement sets up **vibrations**, rapid backwards and forwards movements. These cause changes of pressure in the surrounding air. You can feel sound vibrations if you place your fingertips against your throat as you speak, or gently touch a bicycle bell as it rings. **Sound waves** are created when these changes of pressure spread out in all directions, like the waves on the surface of a pond when someone throws a stone into it.

You can see the effects of the vibrations of a tuning fork after you have struck it, if you dip it in a glass of water.

BASIC FACTS

- Sound is caused by objects vibrating.
- Vibrations transfer energy as a wave through solids, liquids, and gases.
- Sound travels fastest through solids and slowest through gases.
- Sound cannot travel through a vacuum.
- Sounds travel much more slowly than light.
- Frequency is measured in units called hertz (Hz). 1Hz = 1 wave per second.
- Increasing the amplitude of a sound wave makes it sound louder.
- Increasing the frequency of a sound wave gives it a higher pitch.
- Ultrasound is high-frequency sound above human hearing.
- Sound is used in communication.
- Music is pleasant sound which provides relaxation, recreation, and entertainment.
- Echoes are reflected sound.
- The time taken for an echo to be heard can be used to measure distances.
- Sound levels are measured in decibels (dB).
- Noise is unwanted or unpleasant sound.
- Loud noises can damage the ears and be harmful to the general health of a person.
- Prolonged noise can damage the hearing, cause sleeplessness, ill health and stress, interrupt communication, and make it difficult to concentrate.

OXFORD
UNIVERSITY PRESS

Sound, like light, is a form of **energy** and can travel from one place to another. However, light energy can travel much faster than sound energy. Your ears can detect sound energy. But unlike light energy, sound waves cannot travel through empty space. They need a solid, liquid, or gas to pass through. Astronauts on the Moon use radios to speak to each other. Even if they were able to live outside their space suits, they would not be able to talk to each other as they do on Earth. This is because the Moon has no atmosphere through which sound waves could travel.

Sound and a vacuum

One way to show that sound cannot travel through a vacuum is to place a ringing alarm clock inside a bell jar, which is connected to a vacuum pump (a pump which can pump the air from the bell jar). While there is air in the bell jar, the clock can be heard ringing. This is because the vibrating bells make the air inside the jar vibrate. This makes the walls of the jar vibrate, which in turn makes the air outside vibrate—enabling us to hear the sound of the clock.

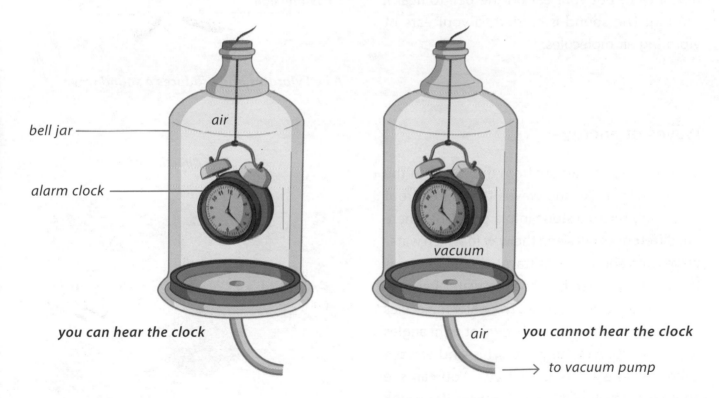

bell jar

air

alarm clock

vacuum

you can hear the clock

air **you cannot hear the clock**

→ to vacuum pump

When the vacuum pump has sucked the air out of the jar, you can no longer hear the clock, even though it is still ringing. There is no air to carry the vibrations and so, with nothing to vibrate. Hence the sound cannot travel.

Vibrations and sound waves

A hand bell vibrates when you shake it—its sides move backwards and forwards rapidly. The vibrating bell pushes to and fro on the air molecules around it, making the air pressure rise and fall. These pressure changes are passed on by the air molecules around the bell. A sound wave travels away from the bell. The parts of the sound wave where the air pressure is greater, as the air molecules are bunched up, are called **compressions**. The parts of the sound wave where the pressure is less, as the air molecules are spread out, are called **rarefactions**. You do not have to put your ear on the bell to hear it ringing. The sound is carried to your ears by vibrating air molecules.

A bell vibrates and produces a sound wave.

Waves of energy

Sound waves spread out from the source of the sound, rather like the waves that spread out when you throw a stone into a pond. But there are differences between the way in which water waves and sound waves travel. When a stone is thrown into water, it is not the water which is moving out from the splash. The water molecules are simply bobbing up and down at right angles to the direction of the waves. This kind of wave is known as a **transverse wave**. You can see another example of a transverse wave if you look at a buoy on the sea or a lake. As a wave passes by, the buoy bobs up and down as the wave of energy passes on. But the buoy does not actually travel in the direction of the wave.

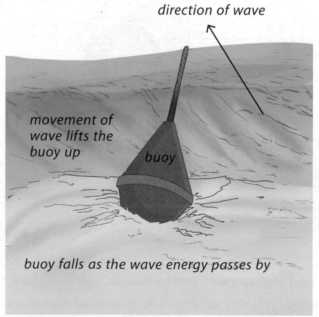

In a transverse wave on the sea, a buoy bobs up and down, but it does not move in the direction of the wave.

OXFORD
UNIVERSITY PRESS

When a sound wave travels through the air, the air molecules vibrate in the same direction as the sound wave is travelling. This kind of wave is known as a **longitudinal wave**.

You cannot see a sound wave, but a slinky spring shows you how longitudinal waves travel. If you hold the spring between your outstretched hands and pull one end of the spring in and out, you can send a longitudinal wave along the spring. The coils of the spring move closer together, then further apart as the wave transfers energy along the spring.

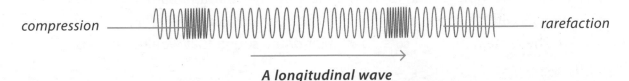

compression   *rarefaction*

A longitudinal wave

Speed of sound

You have seen that sounds cannot travel through a vacuum, because sound vibrations need atoms or molecules to carry them from one place to another. However, sounds can travel through gases. In fact, most of the sounds you hear travel to your ears through the air. In air the speed of sound is about 330 metres per second. The exact speed depends upon the temperature. Sound loses energy as it travels and a loud sound fades after it has travelled for some distance.

Dolphins produce underwater sounds to 'speak' to each other and to find their way.

Sound travels faster through liquids and loses its energy less rapidly than it does through the air. This is because the particles in a liquid are much closer together than they are in air or some other gas. As a result, underwater sounds travel further before dying away. You can hear sounds when you are swimming underwater. Whales and dolphins use underwater sounds to 'speak' to each other and to find their way. Some kinds of whales produce 'songs' that carry for hundreds of kilometres through the oceans. Sound travels at 1,483 metres per second in water at 20°C.

Sounds travel fastest of all through solids because the particles are packed tightly together and they pass on their pulses of sound more quickly. When you press your ear to a wall, you can hear sounds from the next room quite clearly. Sound travels at about 3,600 metres a second through brick, 4000 metres per second in wood, 5,100 metres per second in iron and aluminium, and 6000 metres per second through glass.

How far sound vibrations travel before they lose all their energy depends on what they are travelling through. For example, sound can travel much further through hard solids than through soft materials with air in them. That is why thick curtains can be useful if you live near a busy road. The curtain material cuts down a lot of the sound that would otherwise enter the room.

Frequency and pitch

Sound waves can be detected by a microphone. The microphone changes the sound waves into electrical signals and these can be made to show up on the screen of an oscilloscope. If a tuning fork vibrates to make a single musical note, it makes a wave on the oscilloscope screen.

The wavelength of a sound is the distance between peaks on the wave. Longer waves are lower in energy. Shorter waves are higher in energy. In one wavelength, the wave goes through one complete vibration. The frequency of sound is the number of sound waves being sent out per second. If the frequency increases, you see more waves on the oscilloscope screen and the peaks of the waves are closer together.

Frequency is measured in units called hertz (Hz). If a sound has a frequency of, say 100Hz, then 100 sound waves are being sent out every second. The higher the frequency, the higher the note sounds. Musicians say that it has a higher pitch

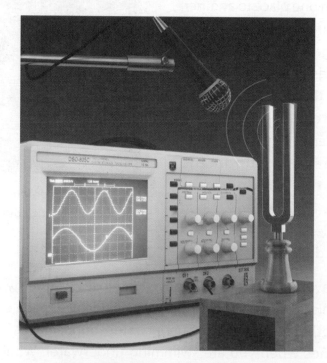

A tuning fork makes a wavy line appear on the oscilloscope screen.

OXFORD
UNIVERSITY PRESS

A whistle makes a very high-pitched sound. The vibrations are very fast at about 10,000Hz. A drum makes a very low-pitched sound of about 20Hz. Its vibrations are quite slow compared to those made by a whistle.

Every sound has a frequency. Human ears can detect frequencies between 20 vibrations a second and 20,000 vibrations a second. As you get older, you become less sensitive to high-pitched sounds. However, some animals, such as bats and dogs, can hear much higher-pitched sounds than we can.

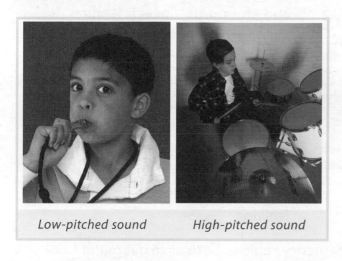

Low-pitched sound   High-pitched sound

We cannot hear the high-pitched sounds made by a dog whistle, but a dog can.

Volume and amplitude

Some sounds are very loud, such as the noise of thunder or of a lorry speeding by. Other sounds are very soft, such as a mouse rustling amongst dead leaves. To compare the loudness or **volume** of different sounds, you can again use a microphone and oscilloscope. Look at the waves produced by these two sounds. The pitch and the wavelength of the two sounds are the same, but the height (or depth) of the wave is different. This is called the **amplitude**. The louder the sound, the more energy it has and the greater is the amplitude.

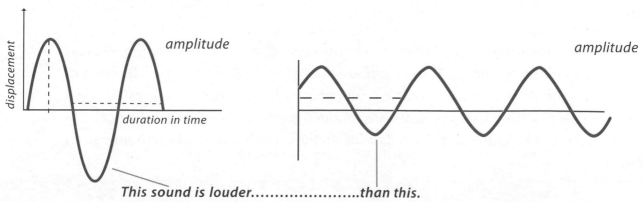

This sound is louder......................than this.

Sounds in our everyday lives

The siren of a fire engine warns us to get out of the way.

From the ringing of the doorbell, to the thump of our heartbeat when we are frightened, sounds give us information about what is happening inside our bodies and around us. Speech is our main method of communication. If you have ever lost your voice you know how difficult it is to make people understand you. Because we are able to talk, we can teach other people and learn from them. We can discuss our ideas, opinions, fears, and feelings.

Sounds can also act as warning signals. Sirens on emergency vehicles warn us to get out of the way. Fire alarms and smoke alarms tell us a building is on fire and that we should get out quickly for our own safety. A burglar alarm ringing at a house, bank, or shop tells us that there may be a robbery in progress.

Telephones allow us to talk to people far away, while radios and televisions can tell us what is happening locally and in places all around the world. Music is sound which is pleasant to our ears. All musical instruments work by making air vibrate, and soft, soothing music is produced which can help reduce stress. Music is also a form of entertainment and recreation and many people enjoy going to concerts and performances of all kinds.

Music

Musical instruments make sound waves at frequencies which we find pleasing. Musical sounds are organised into notes. These notes are then put together as music. The pitch of every note is a certain frequency. A scale is a sequence of notes. Harmony is created when two or more notes with different pitches are sounded together. The length of a note can vary too. The mix of long and short sounds adds rhythm, which is a very important part of all music.

OXFORD
UNIVERSITY PRESS

Musical instruments

All musical instruments make vibrations. They are designed so the vibrations produce musical notes. There are three main types of instruments. Stringed instruments make notes from vibrating strings. Wind instruments have to be blown, while percussion instruments have to be struck.

Stringed instruments include guitars, violins, harps, and pianos. Sometimes the sound that is heard is amplified by a wooden sound box. This means that the sound is made louder by increasing the amplitude. There are three things that affect the sound produced by the vibrating string.

i. *The length of the string:* Long strings vibrate at low frequencies, while short strings vibrate at higher frequencies. A piano has strings of different lengths to produce a range of frequencies.

ii. *The tension of the string:* The more a string is stretched, the higher the frequency of the note it produces. When musicians 'tune up' they alter the tension of the strings, so as to get the pitch exactly right.

iii. *The thickness of the string:* Thick strings give lower frequencies than thin strings because they vibrate more slowly.

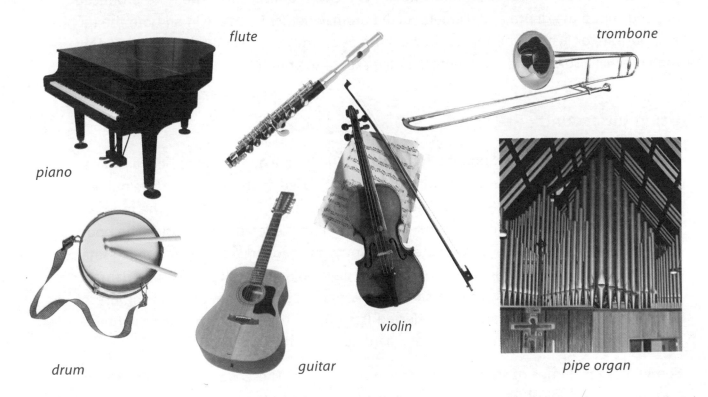

flute

trombone

piano

drum

guitar

violin

pipe organ

Percussion instruments produce sounds when they are hit, scraped, shaken, or banged.

Stringed instruments produce sounds when their stretched strings are plucked or scraped. A guitar and a violin sound very different even if they are playing the same note. When an instrument makes a note, lots of different vibrations are produced. One of these vibrations will make the pitch of the note. It will be the loudest. Any other vibrations will be much quieter. The sound that we hear is made up of all these vibrations. A violin will make one collection of vibrations and a guitar will make a slightly different collection. That is why they sound different.

Wind instruments make sounds by allowing air to vibrate in tubes of different lengths. They include recorders, flutes, trumpets, trombones, and pipe organs. The length of the vibrating air column is controlled by opening and closing valves or by changing the length of the instrument. When air vibrates in a short thin tube, a very high note is produced. A deep note is produced by a long, thick tube. A pipe or concert organ has many pipes of different sizes to produce a range of different notes. In a flute, the length of the column of air is altered by changing the positions of the fingers over the various holes, so altering the length of the tube. In this way, a range of notes can be produced by the one tube.

Percussion instruments produce sounds when they are hit, scraped, shaken, or banged. A drum, for example, produces a note when it is hit with a drumstick. The note produced depends upon the depth and diameter of the drum, whether it has a skin on both the top and bottom, or just on the top, and what type of drumstick is used to hit it. The pitch of the note will also depend upon how tight the skin of the drum is.

Using ultrasound

We cannot hear all sounds. Sounds which are too high for the human ear to hear are called **ultrasonic sounds** or **ultrasound**. Ultrasound can be used to check on the development of a baby inside its mother's body. An ultrasound transmitter is moved over the mother's body. A detector picks up sound waves reflected from the different layers inside the body. The signals are processed by a computer, which puts an image on a screen. It is much safer to use ultrasound rather than X-rays to examine a developing baby, because X-rays damage body cells. Ultrasound is also much safer for the patient and the doctor than the use of X-rays. In addition, X-rays are only reflected from hard surfaces such as bone, whereas ultrasound is reflected from both soft and hard tissues of the body.

Sometimes tiny lumps of solid matter grow in the kidneys. These are called kidney stones and they cause a lot of pain. A beam of ultrasound can make the kidney stones vibrate so much that they break up and can be passed harmlessly out of the body.

A very strong beam of ultrasound can even melt metal. Metal shapes can be cut out this way, or two pieces of metal can be joined together by melting them where they touch. They are then left to cool. This is called ultrasonic welding.

Using echoes

Sounds can be reflected, just like light. A reflected sound is called an **echo**. Some animals use echoes to help find their way around or to help them find their food.

Bats can hear much higher-pitched sounds than we can. Bats produce short bursts of high frequency sounds or ultrasound, in order to find their way around and hunt insect food. Bats detect the size and position of objects by listening to the echoes produced by the sounds. The use of echoes to measure distance is called **echolocation**.

A dolphin is able to find its way through muddy water and find its fish food by using echolocation. It makes clicking sounds in its nostrils. These clicks are focussed into a 'beam' of sound. When the sound waves from the clicks hit an object, some of the energy of the sound is reflected back towards the dolphin. The dolphin picks up these echoes as vibrations in its jaw. The time between the click and the echo tells the dolphin how far away the object is.

Echolocation can also be used on ships to measure the depth of the water beneath them. A pulse of sound is sent down to the sea bed. A detector on the bottom of the ship measures how long it takes for the echo to come back. The longer the echo takes, the deeper the water. A microchip can work out the depth and display it on a screen. Some fishing boats use similar equipment to detect shoals of fish.

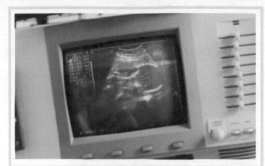

Ultrasound allows the doctor to see how a baby is developing inside its mother's body.

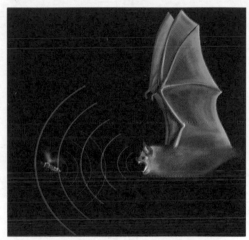

A bat uses ultrasound to find its way around and to catch its insect prey.

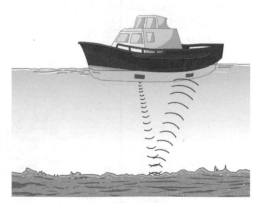

Boats and ships use echolocation to calculate the depth of water beneath them.

Noise

Unwanted or unpleasant sounds are what we call noise. Noise can be annoying. It can also disturb our sleep, interrupt conversations, and cause stress and ill health. Loud noise can also damage our ears and hearing.

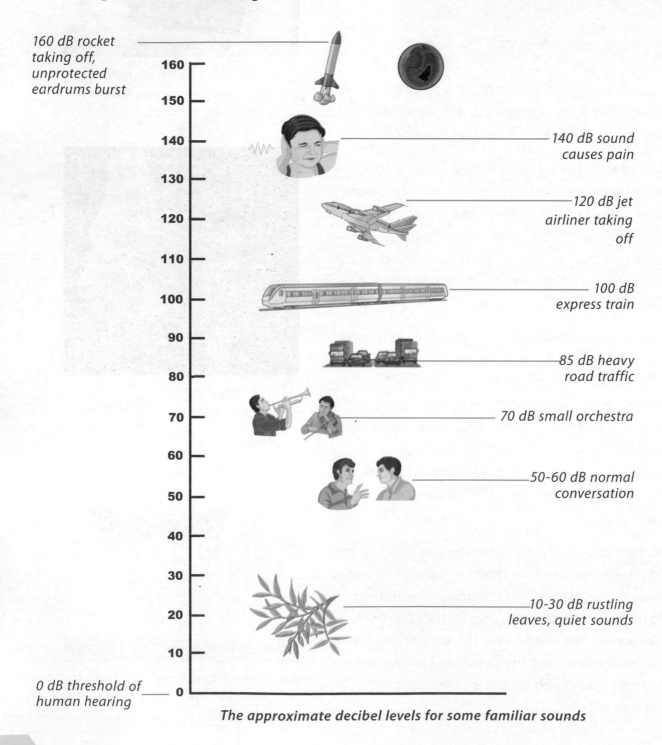

160 dB rocket taking off, unprotected eardrums burst

140 dB sound causes pain

120 dB jet airliner taking off

100 dB express train

85 dB heavy road traffic

70 dB small orchestra

50-60 dB normal conversation

10-30 dB rustling leaves, quiet sounds

0 dB threshold of human hearing

The approximate decibel levels for some familiar sounds

Our early ancestors hunted animals and gathered nuts, berries, and other parts of plants for food. This was a quiet life. As a result, our ears are adapted to fairly quiet sounds. Sounds are measured in units called decibels (dB). The decibel scale starts at 0 dB, and this is a sound which the average human ears can just detect. A sound intensity of 10 dB has ten times as much energy as 0 dB, while 20 dB has a hundred times more energy. The sound level of normal conversation is about 60 dB, which is a million times more energy than 0 dB. Long exposure (more than 8 hours a day) to sounds of 85 dB is considered to be harmful to hearing, whereas 140 dB, the level sometimes reached by indoor rock concerts, can cause pain and will damage the ears within a short time. At 160 dB the eardrums will burst.

People who have to work surrounded by loud noises should wear ear protectors to muffle the noise.

Absorbing sounds

Large, empty rooms often sound hollow and even the smallest sounds seem to be repeated a few times. These repeated noises are echoes. They are made when sound waves bounce off the hard walls and floor, and the echo arrives back a moment after the original sound.

Echoes can be a nuisance in concert halls and recording studios. In a concert hall, soft materials like carpets and thick curtains help to absorb sound waves, so do the clothes of the audience. Many large concert halls have specially-designed sound absorbers on the ceiling so that there are fewer echoes.

Echoes can be a nuisance in a concert hall......   *and in a recording studio.*

Questions

1. What do sound and light have in common?

2. In your own words, describe how sounds are made.

3. Explain how sound is carried from a drum to your ears.

4. Explain why, during a thunderstorm, we often see a flash of lightning before we hear the thunder.

5. Define amplitude, frequency, wavelength, pitch, loudness, and longitudinal and transverse waves.

6. Science fiction films sometimes show gun battles between spacecraft. What would you hear if an enemy spaceship exploded near you? Explain your answer.

7. In your own words, explain how the shape of a musical instrument can affect the sounds it produces.

8. What is an echo?

9. Explain why there are fewer echoes in the school hall when it is full of children than when it is empty.

10. Why can we not hear ultrasound?

11. Why do theatres and cinemas have thick curtains hanging along the walls?

12. Describe how a ship might try to find a sunken wreck that was carrying treasure.

13. What is noise? Name three harmful effects of noise.

14. Name three jobs where you think the people should wear ear protectors.

15. Why can it be harmful to live very near the part of an airport where aircraft take off?

OXFORD
UNIVERSITY PRESS

Things to do

1. When you go home today, make a list of ten unnecessary sounds which you think help to increase the amount of noise pollution in the local streets.

2. Record your voice with a tape recorder and then play back your recording. Why do you think your voice sounds different from the one you hear when you speak?

3. On page 146, we learned that vibrations produce sound waves in the air. You can see the effects of sound waves if you blow up a large balloon and tie the neck. Holding the balloon in your fingers, place it near to a radio or television set that is playing quite loudly. Can you feel the balloon vibrating? This is the way your eardrum vibrates. How far away from the radio or television set can you still feel the vibrations made by the sound waves? Now hold a thin sheet of paper in front of the loudspeaker of a radio or television. Can you feel the vibrations made by the sound waves?

4. Examine a range of musical instruments. See how they produce different sounds. Notice how the shape of the instrument affects the sounds it produces.

Circuits and electric currents

CHAPTER 13

BASIC FACTS

- An electric current is a flow of electrons through a conductor such as a metal.

- A conductor allows electricity to flow through it, but an insulator does not.

- Electrical energy, from a cell, battery or the mains, pushes the current around a circuit.

- Electrical energy is changed to other forms of energy in the components of a circuit.

- We measure electric current in amperes (A) using an ammeter.

- Voltage, tells us about the energy provided by a cell, battery, or the mains. It is measured in volts (V) using a voltmeter.

- The current is the same all around a series circuit.

- In a parallel circuit each bulb (or other component) forms a complete circuit with the cells.

- A circuit diagram is a shorthand way of showing how to connect the components in a circuit.

- Electrical energy is used up in a circuit but current is not.

- Electrical energy used in the home is usually measured in kilowatt-hours (kWh).

- The resistance in a circuit can produce heat and light.

- Fuses and circuit-breakers are devices that switch off an electric current before injury or fire results.

- The earth wire in a circuit directs the current from a faulty appliance into the ground, so that it does not cause an electric shock to anyone handling it.

- Electricity can be used to decompose (split) certain compounds in a process called electrolysis.

- Electricity can also be used to coat materials with a thin layer of metal, in a process called electroplating.

- A conductor carrying an electric current has a magnetic field around it.

- An electromagnet makes use of the magnetic effect of an electric current.

- Electromagnets are used in a wide variety of everyday objects, including electric bells, electric motors, telephones, and loudspeakers.

- An electric motor changes electric energy into movement.

Electricity can make a piece of cling-film stick to your hand. If your hair is dry, a plastic comb may make your hair stand on end. This kind of electricity is called **static electricity**. Electricity can travel along wires to light or heat your home or school. It can make the sky light up during a flash of lightning. As different as these forms of electricity may seem, they all have one thing in common. They all come from atoms and they are all caused by the movements of negatively charged electrons from one material to another.

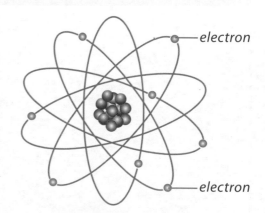

electron

electron

A simplified, and much enlarged view of an atom

OXFORD
UNIVERSITY PRESS

In an atom (see Chapter 8), there are two types of **electric charge**. Electrons have a **negative** (−) charge, while protons have a positive (+) charge. Atoms normally have the same number of electrons as protons, so the charges cancel each other out.

But electrons do not always stay as part of atoms. When you rub certain materials together, they become electrically charged. The friction between the two materials causes electrons to be removed from one of

Static electricity can make your hair stand on end!

them and added to the other. A material that gains electrons becomes negatively charged. The material that loses the electrons becomes positively charged. These charges stay where they were produced if the material is an **insulator**, as when you rub a plastic comb on a piece of cloth and then hold it above tiny pieces of tissue paper. However, when you switch on a light, the 'electricity' flowing through the wires is a flow of electrons—the electrons are able to move. We call a flow of electrons like this an electric **current**.

Conductors and insulators

Some materials allow electrons to flow through them. These materials are called **conductors**. In a conductor, some electrons are not tightly held to their atoms. This means that they are free to move through the material. Air and water can conduct, but only if they contain **ions**. Ions are charged particles formed when an atom (or group of atoms) gains or loses one or more electrons. In gases and liquids, ions are free to move and so they can carry their charges from one place to another.

Insulators are materials which do not let electrons flow through them. Their electrons are held tightly to atoms and are not free to move.

Semiconductors are 'in-between' materials. They are insulators when cold, but become conductors when warm. They are used in microchips in computers and other electronic equipment. They are also found in the light emitting diodes which display letters and numbers in digital instruments, such as calculators and watches, and in certain lasers.

The table below shows some examples of conductors, semiconductors, and insulators:

Conductors	Semiconductors	Insulators
Good:		
metals, especially		**plastics**, e.g.
silver	silicon	PVC
copper	germanium	polystyrene
aluminium		Perspex
carbon		
Poor:		
human body		glass
water		rubber
air		

A simple circuit

A **cell** or **battery** can make electrons move. But there must be a conducting material, such as a piece of copper wire or some other metal, between its two **terminals**. Then a chemical reaction inside the battery will push electrons out of the negative (–) terminal and round to the positive (+) terminal.

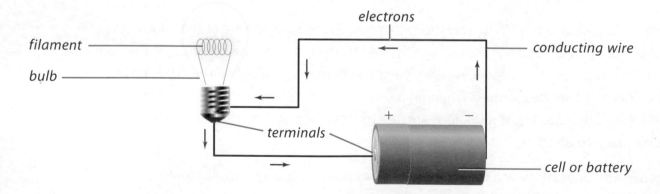

A simple circuit

The cell in the picture above is being used to light up a torch bulb. The conducting path through the bulb, wires, and cell is called a **circuit**. As the electrons pass through the thin wire or **filament**, inside the bulb they make it heat up so that it glows.

OXFORD
UNIVERSITY PRESS

There must be a complete circuit for the current to flow. If the circuit is broken anywhere, the flow of electrons stops and the bulb goes out. Turning the switch OFF breaks the circuit by separating two contacts.

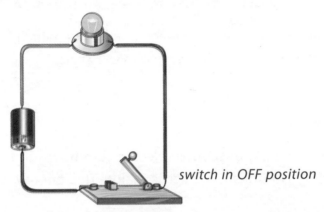

switch in OFF position

How a switch cuts off the flow of electrons

Current and energy

In the circuit shown in the picture above, the cell or battery is giving the electrons energy as it pushes them out. The electrons are spending the energy when they flow through the bulb. The energy is given off as heat.

Sometimes the current passing round a circuit may be so small that it is not enough to light a bulb. Or it may be too large and cause the bulb to burn out, or 'blow'. An **ammeter** is an instrument which gives an accurate measurement of the electric current flowing in a circuit. Current is measured in **amperes (A)**. The larger the current, the greater the flow of electrons and the greater the number of amperes.

To measure the current, the ammeter is connected into the circuit like this:

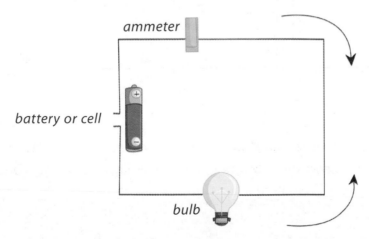

ammeter

battery or cell

bulb

The ammeter can be connected anywhere in this particular circuit because the current is the same all the way round the circuit.

Small currents are sometimes measured in **milliamperes (mA)**. 1000 mA = 1A

Ammeters are either digital, which are easy to read, or analogue which, like the one in the picture on the previous page, have a needle moving over a scale.

Voltage

As we saw earlier, energy is needed to push an electric current around a circuit. A cell or battery provides this energy, so does the electric mains. This energy is called electrical energy.

Voltage tells us how much energy is provided by a cell, battery, or the mains to push an electric current around a circuit. Voltage is measured in **volts**, using a **voltmeter**.

Batteries and cells have a voltage printed on the side. The higher the voltage, the more energy each electron is given, and the more energy it has to spend as it flows round the circuit. The voltage of a cell or battery can be measured by connecting a voltmeter across the terminals.

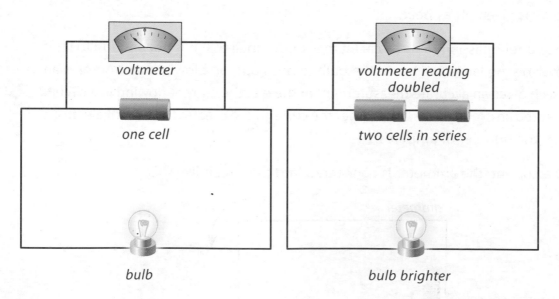

voltmeter

one cell

bulb

voltmeter reading doubled

two cells in series

bulb brighter

If two identical cells are connected in **series** (in a line), the total voltage is twice as much as what it was before. Also, the bulb glows more brightly because a higher current is being pushed through it.

Series and parallel circuits

There are two different ways of adding an extra bulb to the circuit shown in the picture on the previous page. When the bulbs are arranged in **series** (in a line), the bulbs glow dimly. The current from the cell passes through each bulb in turn. It is more difficult for the electrons to pass through two bulbs than one, so there is less energy than before. However, the current is the same at all points in the circuit.

Adding more bulbs makes them even dimmer. And if one bulb is removed or there is a break anywhere in the circuit, all the bulbs go out. Fairy lights are usually arranged in a series circuit and if one bulb goes out so do the others.

In a **parallel circuit** with two bulbs, both bulbs glow brightly because each is getting the full voltage from the cell or battery. However, together, two bright bulbs take

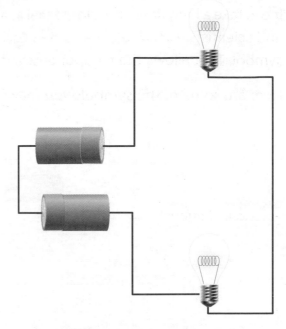

Two bulbs and two cells in series

more current than a single bright bulb, so the cell or battery will not last as long. If one bulb is removed from the parallel circuit, there is still a complete circuit through the other bulb, so it keeps glowing brightly. The current is not the same in all parts of the circuit. The current in each branch will depend on the components in that branch. You can even have a separate switch for each bulb or other component, in a parallel circuit. The electricity supply in our homes uses parallel circuits, so do almost all electrical appliances.

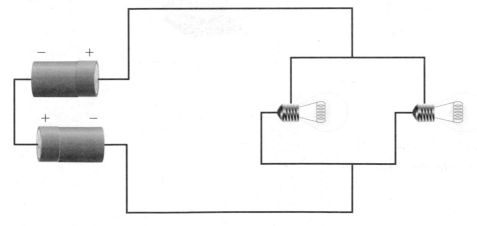

Two bulbs connected in parallel circuit to two cells

Circuit diagrams

It can take a long time and a lot of skill as an artist to draw pictures of circuits. That is why electricians and scientists use **circuit diagrams**. Each component used in a circuit is shown using a particular symbol. That allows the components and the connections to be shown in a very clear way.

Here are some of the symbols you may find useful when you draw circuits:

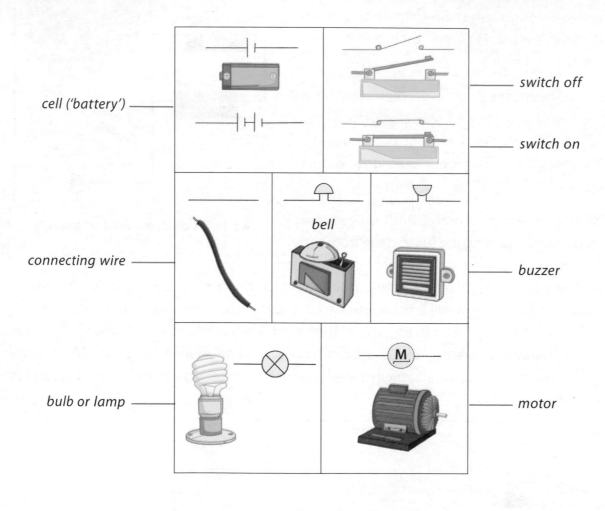

In this circuit diagram, you can see the parallel circuit above, drawn using symbols.

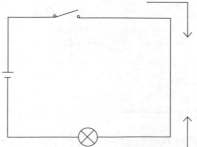

Resistance

A torch bulb does not conduct electricity as well as the connecting wires in a circuit. Scientists say that bulbs have more **resistance** to the flow of electricity. Energy has to be used to overcome this resistance and the bulb gives off this energy as light and heat. Anything that slows down the flow of electricity in a circuit is said to have a resistance.

It may help to think of resistance in terms of a crowd of children crossing the school playground to go to their classes. If the playground is wide, they can move quickly. When they get inside the school, if the corridor is wide, they can still move quite quickly. If the corridor suddenly narrows, the children will be slowed considerably and they may well become hot and bothered trying to push their way through the narrow gap.

Even the best electrical conductor resists an electric current to some extent. That means it slows the movement of electrons through it. How much the current slows down depends on three things. It depends on what kind of material the electrons are moving through. Nichrome resists an electric current more than copper. Resistance also depends on the thickness and the length of the material the electrons are moving through. A long, thin nichrome wire has a higher resistance than an equally long and thin copper wire. A long, thick copper wire has more resistance than a short piece of the same copper wire.

Resistors

A **resistor** is a part of an electrical circuit that is put there to limit the amount of electric current that flows through the circuit. There are two kinds of resistors. **Fixed resistors** have a set resistance. They are mainly used to reduce the flow of electricity through a circuit and reduce the dangers caused by overheating.

Fixed resistors come in several shapes and sizes

Resistors can be connected in both series or parallel circuits. The more resistors are added to a series circuit, the greater the resistance to the current flowing around the circuit. In a parallel circuit, each resistor provides an alternative route for the current to follow, while overall resistance decreases.

A **variable resistor** contains a long coil of nichrome wire. In the picture overleaf, a variable resistor is being used to control the brightness of a bulb. Sliding the control to the right increases the resistance of the circuit, so the bulb gets dimmer.

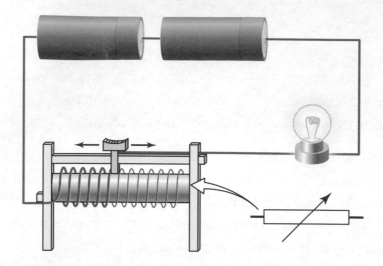

A variable resistor being used to control the brightness of a torch bulb

A variable resistor can be used to dim the lights in a room. The volume control on a typical radio is also a variable resistor, while some model electric car and train sets also use a variable resistor to control the speed of the car or train.

Heat and light from resistance

When an electric current is forced through a conductor against its resistance, the electrons collide with the atoms of the conductor, making them vibrate faster. Some of the electrical energy is changed to heat energy and this makes the temperature of the conductor rise. This is used in electrical heaters. If the temperature rise is high enough, light is produced, and this is used in electric lamps.

The **heating elements** of such electric appliances as irons, hair driers, kettles, toasters, and rice cookers usually consist of lengths of thin nichrome wire. This is used because it has a high resistance and a high melting point. The connecting wires from the mains plug to the appliance are usually made of quite thick copper wire. This has a low resistance, and so the connecting wire does not get hot when the electric current flows through it.

OXFORD
UNIVERSITY PRESS

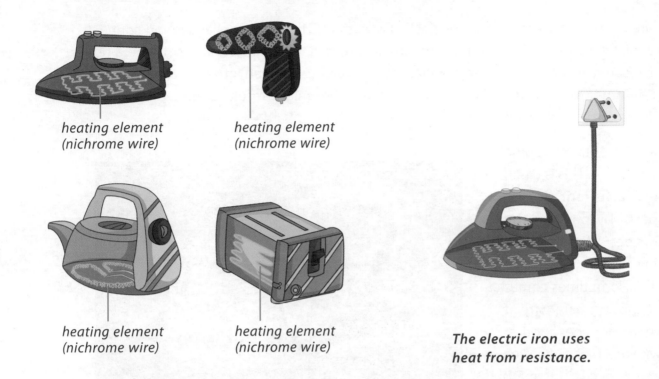

heating element
(nichrome wire)

heating element
(nichrome wire)

heating element
(nichrome wire)

heating element
(nichrome wire)

**The electric iron uses
heat from resistance.**

These are just a few of the electric appliances that use the heating effect of an electric current.

Most electric light bulbs have a coil of thin tungsten wire called the **filament**, in the centre of a sealed glass bulb. When an electric current flows through the high resistance filament, it glows white hot at 1300°C. The bulb is filled with an inert gas such as argon or nitrogen at low pressure. The filament takes quite a long time to burn out because most of the oxygen (needed for burning) has been removed from the bulb.

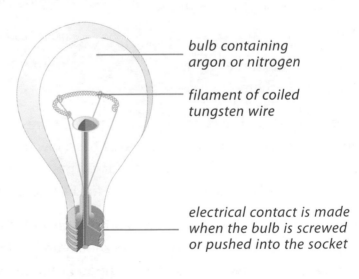

bulb containing
argon or nitrogen

filament of coiled
tungsten wire

electrical contact is made
when the bulb is screwed
or pushed into the socket

Inside a light bulb

Fuses and circuit-breakers

Wires are heated up when they carry an electric current. The more appliances you connect to a parallel circuit, the more current the circuit carries. If, for example, at meal-time a rice cooker, electric kettle, and a toaster or electric fire were all plugged into the same circuit at the same time, the circuit would be overloaded. A fire might result. Overloading is also sometimes caused when an electric motor has to work too hard.

Another cause of overloading is a short circuit. This is when an electric current takes a new path, by-passing the appliance. When wires become old or worn, the insulation sometimes comes away, exposing bare wire. If this live wire touches another bare wire or a piece of metal, a spark may occur. This spark is caused by a sudden large electric current. Short circuits are also caused by faulty wiring.

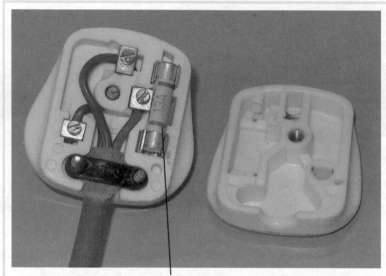

The wire inside this fuse melts to break the circuit.

Fuses come in different shapes and sizes.

Some plugs have a fuse fitted inside them.

Fuses and circuit-breakers are used to prevent fires when an overload takes place. A **fuse** is simply an enclosed length of wire that has a low melting point. It forms the weakest link in a circuit. When a current that is too large passes through the fuse, it heats up and melts, causing a break in the circuit before a fire can develop. We say the fuse has 'blown'.

Fuses come in a variety of shapes and sizes to withstand various electric currents. It is very important that the right type of fuse should be used for each appliance. If a hair drier uses a current of 2A, for example, it is no good fitting its plug with a 1A fuse. The fuse wire will melt almost as soon as the hair drier is switched on. Fitting a 13A fuse is just as silly, because the fuse will not melt until the current reaches 13A. That size of current can do a lot of damage. A 3A fuse is the correct one to fit because it is standard practice to use the next highest fuse value to allow a margin of error.

Circuit-breakers

The problem with fuses is that they work only once. Every time a fuse 'blows', you have to replace it with another one. It can be dangerous to replace fuses in the dark, particularly if all the lights have gone out. Circuit-breakers do the same thing, but you can use them over and over again simply by resetting a switch.

A **miniature circuit-breaker** (MCB for short) is a small electro-magnetic switch. When the electric current is at a safe level, it can flow safely through the circuit-breaker. If the current reaches unsafe levels, the electromagnet is then powerful enough to pull the two halves of the switch apart. The circuit is broken and the electricity shuts off.

A miniature circuit-breaker can be re-set after the problem has been sorted out simply by pressing the switch.

Earth wires

If a 'live' wire comes loose and touches the metal casing of an electric appliance, the metal casing also becomes 'live'. If someone touches the metal casing, the electric current passes through the person's body to the ground. The current can kill, even though it may not be big enough to 'blow' the fuse in the circuit.

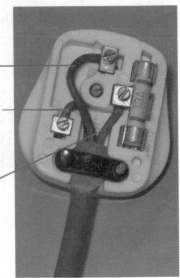

earth wire

neutral wire allows a return path for the electricity

live wire (you should never touch this wire with your bare hands)

The simplest mains supply systems use only two wires

The simplest mains electricity systems use two wires, one of which is live and the other is neutral. This type of system needs only two-pin plugs and sockets. Many mains supply systems have a third wire, the earth wire, in each plug and socket. This is connected to a metal rod in the ground. If a live wire accidentally comes into contact with the metal part of an appliance, the current will flow directly to the ground through the earth wire. It cannot then cause a shock to anyone handling it.

Many mains systems have a third wire, the earth wire. An **earth leakage circuit-breaker** (ELCB for short), is another type of electromagnetic switch. It turns off the electricity supply when the current through the earth wire is greater than 30 milliamperes (30mA). This is a very small current since 1000mA are equal to 1A. An ELCB also breaks the circuit if faulty equipment is used and so prevents the user getting a fatal electric shock.

The chemical effect of an electric current

As well as producing heat and light, electricity can also be used to decompose (split) certain compounds. The process is called **electrolysis**. For electrolysis to work, the compound has to conduct electricity. It also has to be either molten or in solution, and it must contain electrically charged ions that are free to move.

An earth leakage circuit-breaker

Water can be broken down into hydrogen and oxygen by electrolysis. Because water is a weak electrolyte (it has a low concentration of ions), a little dilute sulphuric acid is added to it to speed up the electrolysis. The result is that hydrogen gas collects at the cathode and oxygen at the anode. Because water contains two hydrogen atoms for every oxygen atom (its formula is H_2O), twice as much hydrogen as oxygen is produced.

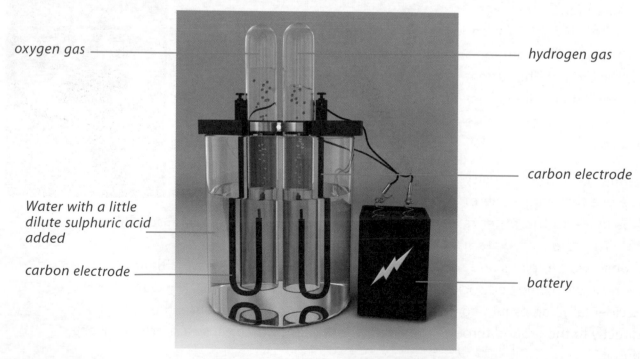

oxygen gas

hydrogen gas

carbon electrode

Water with a little dilute sulphuric acid added

carbon electrode

battery

The electrolysis of acidified water

OXFORD
UNIVERSITY PRESS

Chemicals from salt

Common salt or table salt, sodium chloride, is the starting point for the manufacture of all chemicals that contain either sodium or chlorine. More compounds of sodium are in everyday use than compounds of any other element. Electrolysis of salt solution is the most widely used process for manufacturing chemicals from salt. A current of electricity is passed through salt solution, so that the sodium chloride is split up into sodium and chloride ions. The sodium reacts with water to form a solution of caustic soda (sodium hydroxide, NaOH), which is used to make all other sodium compounds. Chlorine and hydrogen are produced as by-products.

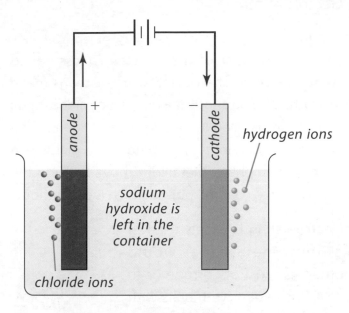

The electrolysis of common salt (sodium chloride)

Purifying copper

Electrolysis can also be used to purify copper. A block of impure copper is used as the anode (the positive terminal), and a sheet of pure copper is used as the cathode (the negative terminal). The two pieces of copper are dipped into copper sulphate solution. When an electric current is passed through the solution, the copper sulphate splits up to form positive (+) copper ions and negative (–) sulphate ions. The copper ions are attracted to the cathode, where they build up as a layer of pure copper. As this happens, copper from the impure block dissolve in the copper sulphate electrolyte to replace the copper ions. In this way, copper is transferred from the impure to the pure sample. The impurities fall to the bottom of the container.

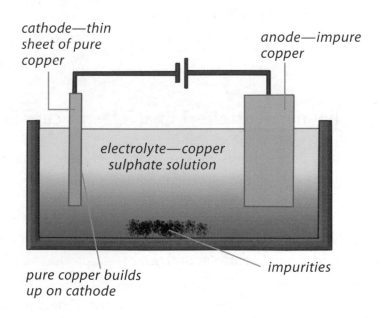

Purifying copper by electrolysis

Electroplating

Coating an object, such as a key or an iron nail, with a thin layer of metal is a process called **electroplating**. The object to be plated is made the cathode. The anode is a pure piece of the metal which is to be used as plating such as copper. The electrolyte contains a compound of this metal such as copper sulphate. Metal ions move through the electrolyte to coat the object which is the cathode.

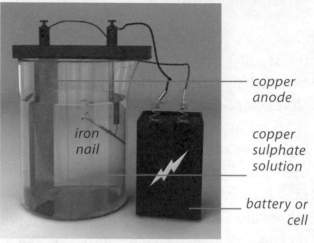

copper anode

copper sulphate solution

battery or cell

iron nail

Copper plating an iron nail

Electroplating is widely used to protect metals that would otherwise rust or corrode or to coat less expensive metals with valuable metals such as gold or silver. Tin cans are made by electroplating steel cans with tin. Car radiators, the handlebars and other shiny parts of bicycles are often made by electroplating steel with chromium.

Gold-plated wrist watch

Chromium-plated car radiator

The magnetic effect of an electric current

Many of the things we see or use every day, including electric bells, electric motors, telephones, and loudspeakers, use electricity to make magnetism.

The connection between magnetism and electricity was first discovered in 1819 by a Danish scientist, Hans Oersted. He found that a wire carrying a strong electric current made a compass needle move. He realized that an electric current was producing magnetism and that a conductor carrying an electric current has a magnetic field around it. This discovery was used by an English scientist, William Sturgeon, in 1825 to make the first electromagnet. This consisted of a soft iron bar with a coil of wire around it. When the current in the coil was switched on, the bar became a magnet. When the current was turned off, the iron bar lost is magnetism.

We now know that electromagnets can be made stronger by increasing the current in the coil, or by increasing the number of turns of wire in the coil. It is because we can turn a magnet on and off that makes electromagnets so very useful. Huge magnets are used to sort and carry scrap iron and steel, and also to move steel objects such as cars. Smaller magnets form an essential part of electric bells, telephones, electric motors, and dynamos.

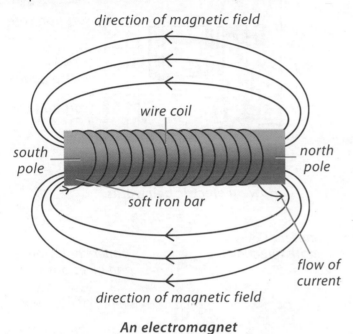

direction of magnetic field

wire coil

south pole

north pole

soft iron bar

flow of current

direction of magnetic field

An electromagnet

An electromagnet sorting and lifting iron and steel at a scrapyard

Uses of electromagnets

A surgeon may use a powerful electromagnet to remove a steel splinter for a patient's eye. Once the magnet is in the right position, the current is switched on and the strong magnetism pulls the splinter from the eye.

Certain trains, called Maglev trains (short for magnetic levitation), give a very quiet and smooth ride. They do not run on rails, but instead, they 'float' above the rails because of electromagnetism. An electric current passes through electromagnets in both the track and train, while the repelling force produced by the magnetism lifts the train upwards.

This Maglev train uses electromagnets to produce a very smooth and quiet ride.

A doorbell or electric bell also uses electromagnetism. When the bell push is pressed, an electric current passes through the electromagnet. An iron bar linked to a small hammer is attracted by the electromagnet, and the bell is struck. The circuit is now broken and the magnet is switched off. A spring pulls the iron bar back to its original position. The whole process is now repeated over and over again to make the familiar ringing sound, until the bell push is released.

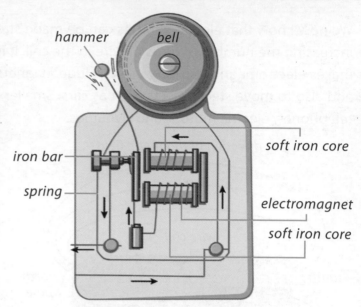

How an electric bell works

Radios, TV sets, CD players, and stage sound-systems have loudspeakers. Some machines have earphones, which are small loudspeakers that fit in the ears. A loudspeaker receives a strong electrical signal and changes the signal into sound waves. In most loudspeakers, the electrical signals pass through a wire coil which is wound round the neck of a paper cone. This coil acts as an electromagnet. The coil is suspended inside a permanent magnet. When the current flows one way, the magnetic forces push the electromagnet and the cone outwards. When the current flows the other way, the cone is pulled inwards. The movements of the coil to and fro cause the cone to vibrate and produce sound waves. When these sound waves reach your ears, you hear them as sounds.

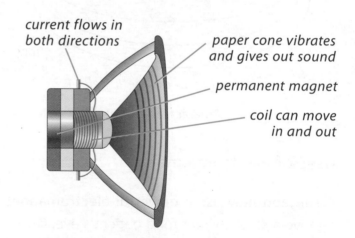

Inside a loudspeaker

The metal detectors used at airports also use electromagnetism. Inside the walls of the arch you walk through are large coils of wire carrying an electric current. If someone goes through the arch carrying a gun or a knife, the metal in the gun or knife alters the magnetic field produced by the coils. This change can be detected and an alarm will sound.

An airport metal detector uses electromagnetism.

OXFORD
UNIVERSITY PRESS

Electric motors

Many of the machines that we use every day are powered by an electric motor. Such a motor changes electrical energy into movement. It makes use of the fact that a coil of wire carrying an electric current produces a magnetic field. This will be attracted or repelled by another magnet.

In a simple electric motor, an electric current is fed into the coil by two carbon rods or other contacts, called brushes. The coil sits between the north and south poles of a permanent magnet. The magnetic fields of the coil and the permanent magnet repel each other, making the coil turn. To keep the motor turning, the current is reversed every half turn by a device called a commutator. The continuous turning action of the coil drives the motor.

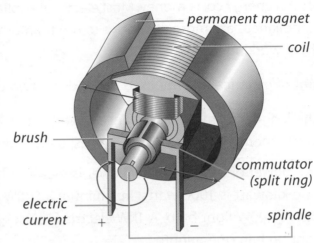

A simple electric motor

electric fan

food mixer

washing machine

refrigerator

vacuum cleaner

hair dryer

Paying for electricity

Using electrical energy costs money. Most electrical appliances get their energy from the mains supply. But some appliances are more expensive to run than others. That is because they need more energy to keep them working.

The amount of electrical energy used depends on two things:

i.   The length of time the appliance is working. A TV or electric fire will use twice as much energy in two hours as it does in one hour.

ii.   The power of the appliance. Power is measured in watts (W) and kilowatts (kW). One kilowatt is 1000 watts. In 1 minute a 500W toaster uses five times more energy than a 100W light bulb. A 1kW electric fire uses ten times more energy than a 100W light bulb in one minute.

kettle 2kW

hair drier 500W

washing machine 1.5kW

iron 1kW

drill 400W

fire 3kW

vacuum cleaner 700W

television set 250W

Electrical appliances normally have their power rating marked on them. If you know the power rating in watts or kilowatts, and the length of time for which the appliance has been working, you can find the energy used from this formula:

electrical energy used = power x time

The electricity passes through an electricity meter as soon as it enters your home. This records how much electricity you have used. The electricity companies charge for units of electricity called kilowatt-hours. This is how to calculate how many of these units have been used:

Number of units of electrical energy used =   power   x   time
(in kilowatt hours)   (in kilowatts)   (in hours)

If a 3kW electric fire is used for 4 hours, then the number of units used = 3 x 4 = 12 units

Using electricity safely

Electricity travels from place to place. It will flow through any conductor that happens to be present. If you happen to be the only conductor around, then the electricity will flow through you. A 12V car battery is unlikely to kill you, although it will give you a nasty shock. A voltage of 50V can be enough to cause severe burns or even kill you.

We use electricity in the home for very many tasks, including heating, cooking, keeping food cool, mixing food, and entertaining us with sound and pictures. If it is used properly and safely, electricity is a wonderful friend. But used carelessly, it can be a deadly enemy.

Here are some safety rules to follow when using electricity or going near power lines:

- Never use an electrical appliance while standing in water or when your hands are wet.

- Never use an appliance in the bathroom while in the bath tub or shower. Keep radios and other appliances away from the bath tub and sink and other wet places.

- Never use appliances that have damaged or bare wires or old or damaged plugs and sockets.

- Never run a wire under a carpet.

- Make sure that all plugs and switches are correctly wired with tight connections. If there is any doubt, ask a qualified electrician to check them.

- Fit a fuse with the correct rating to each electrical appliance.

- Do not overload power sockets.

- Use earthed appliances wherever possible.

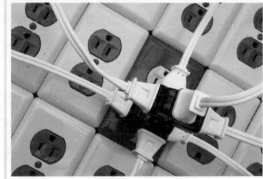

An overloaded socket is dangerous.

- Switch off the mains supply and remove the plug from the socket before attempting any kind of repair or adjustment to an appliance.

- Do not use faulty appliances.

- Do not insert anything into electrical sockets or appliances.

- When outdoors, never climb where electrical wires and cables are strung.

- Never fly a kite or use a fishing rod near power lines.

Questions

1. What is a circuit?

2. What job does a cell or battery do in a circuit?

3. What is not used up in a circuit?

4. Name three good conductors of electricity and three non-conductors or insulators.

5. The table below summarises the differences between a series circuit and a parallel circuit.

   Copy out the table and complete it.

Series circuit	Parallel circuit
	Bulbs stay at the same brightness when you add more bulbs.
The electrical energy in each bulb gets less when you add more bulbs.	
	You can use a separate switch for each bulb.
If one bulb 'blows' they all go out.	

6. What is a circuit diagram? Why do we not draw the real thing every time?

7. What gases are used in a light bulb? What is wrong with using air?

8. What instrument do we use to measure current? What units do we use when we measure current?

9. Describe the working of a doorbell.

10. What are Maglev trains? How do they run?

11. What effect does electric current have on chemicals?

12. What is resistance? Why do we use resistors?

13. What effect does the voltage of a battery have on the amount of current?

14. How many 1.5V cells would you need to provide a voltage of 9V?

15. What is a fuse and what is its purpose?

16. How do fuses differ from circuit-breakers?

OXFORD
UNIVERSITY PRESS

17. What are two things you could do to increase the strength of an electromagnet?

18. Good loudspeakers have their paper cones fixed to a heavy metal frame. Suggest why this is.

19. These pictures show situations where electricity is not being used safely. Explain the danger in each picture.

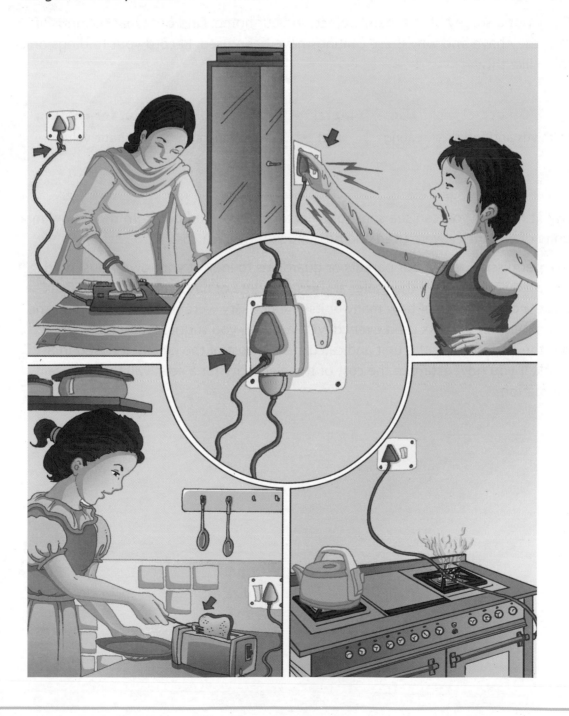

Things to do

1. Look around your home or school. Suggest some ways of saving electricity.

2. Look around your home or school. List all the appliances which use an electric motor.

3. If you can, find a toy which has an electric motor. Look for the motor and then identify the coil, the magnets, the commutator, and the brushes.

4. Carry out a survey of the metal objects in your home. Find out what coatings (if any) they have and why these coatings have been used. Record your findings on a table like this:

Object	Use	Metal	Coating	Reason for coating
knives and forks	eating	steel	silver plating	aesthetic value

5. Ask at home if you can see some old electricity bills. Find out from them how many units of electricity were used and how much they each cost.

6. Ask permission from your parents or guardians to look at your own household electricity meter. Read the meter at the same time of day every day for a week. Make a careful note of how many units of electricity were used each day. Are the same number of units used every day? If not, can you suggest reasons why? Find out the current cost of a unit and calculate the cost of the electricity used in a week. If you now estimate the cost of the electricity for a year, will this be a fair estimation?

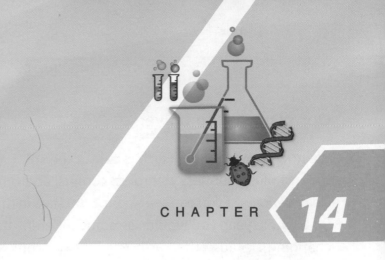

Investigating space

CHAPTER 14

BASIC FACTS

- The universe is all the matter, energy, and space that exists.
- A star is a body in space which generates its own heat and light from nuclear fusion within its core.
- Galaxies are giant collections of many millions of stars.
- The Milky Way is the galaxy to which our Sun belongs.
- Our Sun is a medium-sized star which is made mainly of hydrogen gas, with some helium and small quantities of other elements.
- The Sun generates heat and light from nuclear fusion.
- Scientists believe the Sun began life about 5 billion years ago.
- Space probes and satellites have greatly increased our knowledge about the Sun.
- Distances in space are so large that we measure them in light-years.

- A light-year is equal to the distance travelled by light in one year.
- A constellation is a group of stars in the sky which form a fixed pattern in relation to each other, as viewed from Earth.
- Information about distant stars can be obtained by studying the spectrum they produce.
- A supernova is an immense explosion produced when an old and very massive star uses up its fuel for nuclear fusion and collapses under its own gravity.
- A black hole is a region in space where gravity is so strong that even light cannot escape. It is thought to be formed after a supernova.
- Reflecting telescopes and radio telescopes can be used to study distant stars and planets.
- Scientists believe the universe started forming after a Big Bang some 15 billion years ago.

When you look up at the sky, you are looking out into space. Look up into the night sky and you can see stars and planets and huge expanses of empty space in between. The stars you see on a clear, dark night are millions of miles away and it takes many years for their light to reach your eyes. Our Earth is in fact just a tiny speck in a vast universe. From the earliest times, people have tried to understand how we on Earth fit into our local part of space and into the wider universe.

On a clear night you can see about 2000 stars in the sky, as well as the Moon and planets.

Our place in the universe

We now know that the Earth is part of the solar system, a family of eight planets and their moons, plus countless asteroids, comets, and other objects, all circling the Sun. On a very clear, dark night you can see about 2000 stars in the sky. If you were to study the sky regularly for a whole year, you would see some different stars each season. Your view of space keeps changing because the Earth revolves or orbits around the Sun, a journey which takes a whole year to complete.

The Milky Way Galaxy

The stars we see with the naked eye are just a small proportion of the total numbers that exist in our part of space. This is because our solar system belongs to a great spiral-shaped system of over 500,000 million widely separated stars called the Milky Way Galaxy. A galaxy is a gigantic collection of stars, gas, and dust all held together by the pull of gravity. The Sun, Earth, and all the stars in the Galaxy race around its centre. The Milky Way Galaxy is so huge that it would take you at least 100,000 years to go across it if you could travel at the speed of light.

All the stars we can see in the night sky belong to the Milky Way Galaxy. The Milky Way gets its name because often, to the naked eye, it looks like a splash of milk in the night sky.

The Milky Way has most of its stars at the centre. This gives the Galaxy a central bulge, from which arms spread out, like a gigantic starfish. We live in one of these arms. Like all galaxies, the whole Milky Way is travelling through space, while the stars within it are continuously moving around the centre of the Galaxy. The stars in the Milky Way Galaxy are far apart from each other. On average the distance between each is five light-years. A light-year is the distance that light travels in one year. A light-year is almost 9.5 billion kilometres.

For comparison, if you used footballs to represent the stars, you would have to place them about 8000 kilometres apart to represent this distance. Our Sun is situated in one of the spiral arms of the Milky Way, about two-thirds of the way from the centre.

Other galaxies

Until the 20th century, astronomers thought that the Milky Way Galaxy was the only galaxy in the universe. We now know that beyond the Milky Way, there are millions of other galaxies, each containing millions of stars. These galaxies are extremely far apart from each other. Galaxies come in three basic shapes: spiral, like the Milky Way Galaxy, elliptical, and irregular. Spiral galaxies are made up of young, middle-aged, and old stars, together with huge quantities of gas and dust. Elliptical galaxies are flattened ball-shaped collections of old stars that are near the end of their lives. Elliptical galaxies are the most common type of galaxy in the universe. Irregular galaxies are those that have not formed into a specific shape. They mostly contain bright young stars, some old stars, and large amounts of gas and dust. Irregular galaxies are the rarest type of galaxy in the universe.

The nearest galaxy to our own is called Andromeda. It is just visible as a pale smudge in the sky on clear nights. The starlight reaching us from Andromeda left there around 2.5 million years ago.

An irregular galaxy

The Sun

The Sun is at the centre of our solar system. Indeed, without the Sun, the solar system would not exist. All the planets and their moons, asteroids, comets, and other bodies in our solar system orbit around the Sun. The Sun is a medium-sized star, which means it creates its own light and heat. It is the closest star to the Earth, which is why it looks so large. All the other stars are much further away.

The Sun is a tremendous ball of hot, glowing gases which rotates in space. It is bigger than a million Earths in volume. The centre of the Sun is mainly made of hydrogen gas, with some helium and tiny amounts of other elements. Hydrogen is the Sun's fuel. Within the Sun, nuclear fusion continuously produces massive amounts of energy in the form of light and heat, while helium gas is released. At the centre of the Sun, the temperature is about 15 million°C. The surface temperature is about 5500°C.

The Sun sometimes has dark spots on its surface. These sunspots are areas where the temperature is lower. Sunspots are not always in the same place on the Sun. Scientists have discovered that every eleven years, the Sun has more sunspots than usual. Sometimes a blazing burst of gas comes from the surface of the Sun, shoots up hundreds or even thousands of kilometres into space, and then loops back down. This is a called a prominence. From time to time, there are huge explosions on the Sun and extremely hot gas particles are hurled into space. These solar flares seem to be associated with sunspots. By observing the movement of sunspots, scientists found that different parts of the Sun take different lengths of time to rotate. The Sun's middle, or equator, takes about twenty-five days to rotate completely, whereas its top takes around thirty days.

SAFETY:

Never look at the Sun directly with your eyes, even with sunglasses, and do not look at it through binoculars or through a telescope. You could seriously damage your eyes or even become blind.

Sun facts

- Diameter at equator: 1.4 million km
- Mass: 333,000 times Earth's mass
- Temperature: (surface) 5500°C (centre) 15 million°C
- Weight of hydrogen fuel used: about 600 million tonnes a second
- Average distance from Earth: 150 million km.
- Time taken for sunlight to reach Earth: just over 8 minutes

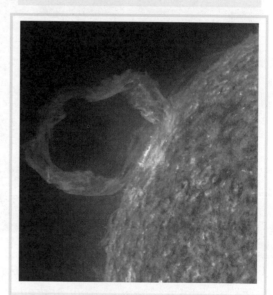

The dark patches on the surface of the Sun are sunspots, while the huge, flame-like object is a prominence.

The birth of the Sun

Scientists believe that the Sun began its life about 5 billion years ago. A great cloud of dust and gas formed in space. This cloud of gas and dust began to form a spinning disc with a huge bulge in the middle. The disc started spinning faster and faster. The huge bulge kept heating up until it began turning hydrogen gas into helium gas. Slowly the great bulge was turning into the Sun. At the same time, the planets, including our Earth, were formed from the rest of the gassy disc.

OXFORD
UNIVERSITY PRESS

The Sun's life

The Sun is about 5 billion years old and, like all living things, it will complete a lifetime and then die. As we have just seen, the Sun's fuel is hydrogen gas, which it turns into helium gas, creating huge quantities of heat and light and many other kinds of radiation. Almost half of the Sun's hydrogen has now been turned into helium. It will take about 5 billion more years for all the hydrogen to be used up. When the last of the hydrogen has been turned into helium, the Sun will start to grow bigger. It will grow up to 100 times its present size and be a 1000 times brighter than it is now. Then it will be called a red giant star. The next stage is that the Sun's outer layers will start turning into a cloud of gas. The gas will slowly disappear and leave only the Sun's centre. The Sun will start to cool down,

In billions of years time, our Sun will look like this white dwarf star.

although this will take millions more years. Stars like this are called white dwarf stars. Finally the Sun will cool down completely and end its life as a cold, dark body called a black dwarf.

Studying the Sun

Spacecraft illustration— SOHO

Our atmosphere makes it very difficult to study the Sun. This is because it filters out many of the Sun's rays. The best way to study the Sun is to send space probes and satellites into space.

The American space probe Ulysses was launched in 1990, and reached the Sun in 1994. It has been sending back information about the Sun's outer layers and solar winds (particles that pour out of the Sun at high speed) ever since. Ulysses was only expected to last for five years, but in 2009 it was still sending back information about the Sun. Unfortunately Ulysses' orbit is taking it further and further away from the Earth, and the information it is sending back is becoming less valuable. The American space probe SOHO (short for Solar and Heliospheric Observatory) has been studying the Sun since 1995, while in February 2010, the American Space Agency NASA launched the Solar Dynamics Laboratory (SDO). This spacecraft will study the inner workings of the Sun and take pictures of the Sun every 0.75 seconds and send them back to Earth.

Constellations

Stars that appear in groups in the night sky called constellations. In ancient times people divided the bright stars they saw into constellations which were named after things they knew. Often these names were those of animals, or of heroes and heroines in their myths. They drew imaginary pictures around the constellations so they were easy to remember.

Forty-eight constellations had been named by the time of the famous Egyptian astronomer Ptolemy, who lived from AD120 to about AD180. More constellations were described later, as people produced new maps of the night sky. In 1930, astronomers decided to divide the whole sky into eighty-eight areas. The old constellation names now refer to these eighty-eight areas, instead

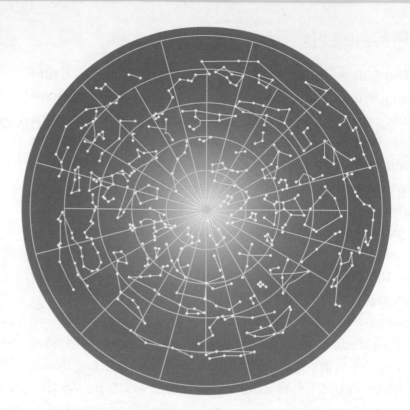

Star map showing the main constellations visible in the northern hemisphere between December and March. The names of the constellations are written in capital letters. The pale area is the Milky Way.

of the mythical figures. You can find a star by knowing which constellation it appears in. For example, knowing that Sirius is in Canis Major, or Betelgeuse is in Orion, helps you to find these stars more quickly.

The constellations you see depend on where you live on the Earth. If you live in Pakistan or somewhere else in the northern hemisphere, there are constellations you will never see unless you travel to the southern hemisphere. Most of the constellations in the southern hemisphere were named by travellers in the 16th and 17th centuries.

The brightest and best-known constellations visible in the northern hemisphere between December and March are shown on the star map above.

You can observe that the Sun, Moon, and planets seem to move through twelve constellations during the year. These twelve are called the constellations of the zodiac. Ancient people believed that these constellations were special. They developed astrology—the study of these bodies and their movements —in order to predict how they thought the constellations would affect human behaviour. Today this belt of constellations is still called the zodiac, but scientists say that there is no proof that astrology can be used to predict the future.

Some constellations can be seen on very clear nights all year round. They circle around the sky without ever sinking below the horizon. These are called circumpolar constellations. Look for them around Polaris, the North Star or Pole Star. As the Earth turns on its axis during the night, you can see these stars move anticlockwise around Polaris. Other constellations rise and set overnight and change with the seasons.

It is important to remember that although the stars in a constellation look as if they are close together, there are in fact immense distances between them. It is simply that we cannot tell this just by looking up at the night sky.

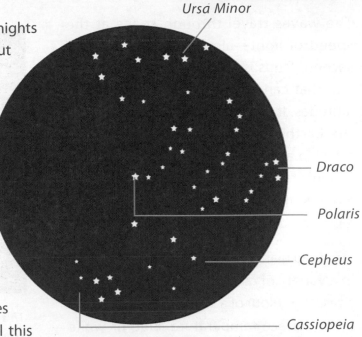

Ursa Minor

Draco

Polaris

Cepheus

Cassiopeia

The circumpolar stars that are visible all year round on clear nights from mid-northern latitudes

Studying other stars

Every one of the stars you see in the night sky is, like our Sun, a violent spinning ball of hot, burning gases. Like our Sun, they produce their own light by nuclear fusion reactions in their centres. You cannot tell just by looking at the stars which ones are shining the most starlight into space. The Sun, for example, looks many times brighter than the other stars, but it is not. How bright a star looks depends not only on how much light it sends out, but also on how far away it is from the Earth. The Sun looks so very bright because it is hundreds of thousands of times closer to us than any other star.

The nearest star to our Sun is called Proxima Centauri. It was discovered in 1915 and is only visible with a telescope from the southern hemisphere. Its light takes 4.22 years to reach the Earth.

These enormous distances prevent us seeing the stars up close, even with the most powerful telescopes. Fortunately, we can learn about the stars by studying the starlight that comes to Earth. The light we see coming from a star is only a small part of the electromagnetic radiation coming from space. We cannot see the ultra-violet, X-rays, gamma rays, and infra-red rays. Each kind of star radiates a different mixture of visible and invisible light waves into space.

The waves travel through space at the speed of light—almost 300,000 km per second. Sirius is the brightest and closest star that can be seen from mid-northern latitudes. It is almost nine light-years from the Earth. This means that if you could travel in a spacecraft at the speed of light, it would take you almost nine years to reach Sirius. At the same speed, it would take only eight minutes to reach the Sun.

From red giants to white dwarfs, stars come in a variety of colours and a huge range of sizes. The colour of a star gives us some idea of its surface temperature. Blue or white stars are hot and they give off the most light; red stars are cooler and their surfaces shine dimly. Astronomers use special equipment to collect and separate the light

This ultra-violet photograph of the red giant star Betelgeuse was taken from the Hubble Space Telescope. Betelgeuse is 1000 times larger than the Sun and it is surrounded by a vast cloud of thin, hot gas.

from a star into a spectrum. This tells them such things as what the star is made of and how hot it is. Many stars give out more infrared light than visible light.

About half of all the 'stars' in the sky are really pairs of stars. This is true of Sirius, the brightest star in the night sky. Although Sirius looks like one bright star, it is actually two stars. Sirius A is a white star with a mass 2.3 times that of the Sun and a diameter 1.8 times that of the Sun. It is also twenty-three times as bright as our Sun, although we cannot see this from Earth because Sirius is so much further way. Sirius is orbited every fifty years by the much dimmer white dwarf star, Sirius B. Sirius B was the first white dwarf star to be discovered.

The end of a star's life

Smaller stars live much longer than large ones though, whether large or small, for most of their lifetime, stars shine without much change. When a star's fuel begins to run out, the star starts to enlarge until it becomes a giant or a supergiant. Stars that are less than one and a half times the Sun's mass then blow off their outer layers, leaving a tiny, cooling star called a white dwarf. Stripped bare of its outer layers, the star then collapses on itself and becomes extremely dense. A white dwarf star, although similar in size to the Earth, has as much mass as the whole Sun. A single teaspoon of it would weigh many tonnes.

If a very large star with a mass more than eight times that of the Sun dies, its core collapses so quickly that it explodes. The explosion is called a **supernova**. The core may remain as either a **neutron star** or a **black hole**. Neutron stars are much denser than white dwarfs. A neutron star weighs more than our Sun, even though all this mass is packed into a ball just 10 kilometres or so

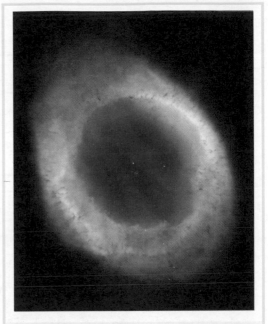

The small dot in the centre of this photograph is the remains of an old star that blew off its outside layers of gas between 5000 and 6000 years ago. It is now a white dwarf star.

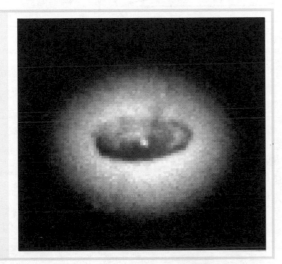

This photograph of a black hole was taken from the Hubble Space Telescope.

across. A black hole is denser than a neutron star. The gravity around it is so strong that not even light can escape. This makes it impossible to see a black hole. Astronomers look for black holes indirectly. A black hole may pull in matter from a nearby visible star, or gas disappearing over the edge of a black hole may send out a burst of X-rays that can be detected.

Telescopes

Small telescopes usually have lenses to make faraway objects look bigger. These telescopes are called **refracting telescopes**. All the world's really large telescopes that are used for studying space use mirrors to make distant objects look nearer or bigger. This is because it is easier to make very large mirrors than it is to make really large lenses. The telescopes which use mirrors are called **reflecting telescopes**

In a reflecting telescope a large concave mirror bounces all the light coming through the telescope barrel into a smaller plane mirror. From there the light is reflected through the eyepiece lens, which bends the light into the eye. A reflecting telescope can collect light from faint objects far away in space.

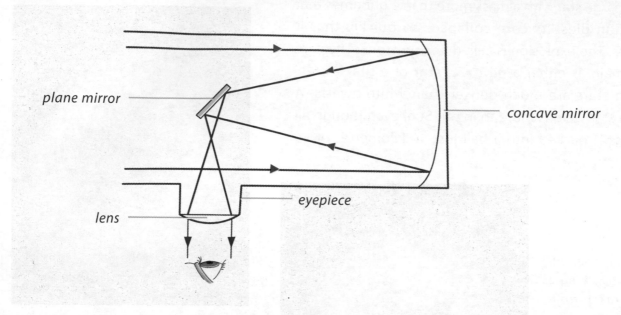

plane mirror

concave mirror

eyepiece

lens

In a reflecting telescope, light bounces off mirrors instead of passing through lenses.

The world's largest reflecting telescope is on the island of La Palma in the Canary Islands. It has a concave mirror 10.4 metres in diameter. Even larger reflecting telescopes are being built. Probably the world's most famous telescope today is the Hubble Space Telescope which was launched in April 1990. Hubble is a reflecting telescope powered by two large solar panels, orbiting nearly 600 km above the Earth. Its main mirror is 2.4 metres in diameter. This is not large compared to the reflecting telescopes on Earth, but because Hubble is above the Earth's atmosphere, it is able to see faraway objects more clearly than any telescope in history.

The world's largest telescopes, like this one at La Palma, use a large concave mirror to collect the light from distant stars.

OXFORD
UNIVERSITY PRESS

Radio telescopes

Radio waves coming from space were first detected in 1931. However, it was not until the late 1940s, that radio telescopes were first built and used. The radio waves are collected and changed into electrical signals that can be used to make radio images or pictures.

Just as you tune in your radio to listen to your favourite music, so radio astronomers can tune their telescopes to pick up radio waves from distant galaxies that are millions of light-years from the Earth. Radio telescopes work like the telescopes that collect light from space. A dish faces the sky to

The Arecibo Radio Telescope in Puerto Rico is the world's largest.

collect and focus the waves. However, because radio waves have a much greater wavelength than that of light waves, a radio telescope has to be much larger than an optical telescope to collect the same amount of information. The world's largest radio telescope is at the Arecibo Radio Observatory in Puerto Rico. Its bowl-shaped dish is 305 metres in diameter. It is built in a natural hollow in the jungle and as the Earth moves, the dish points to a different part of the sky.

Sometimes instead of one enormous dish-aerial, lots of smaller radio telescopes are used together. A computer then combines the information provided by the separate dishes. The largest radio telescope of this type is on an isolated plain near Socorro in New Mexico. It consists of twenty-seven dishes, each 25 metres in diameter. They are arranged along three arms shaped like the letter 'Y'.

An aerial photograph of the 27 radio telescopes near Socorro in New Mexico

How the universe began

There are 100,000 million galaxies in the universe and everything that scientists know about the galaxies in our universe comes from the radiation they send out. As a result of measuring the movement of the galaxies, scientists believe that the whole of the universe is expanding. Space itself is getting bigger and so the galaxies are moving further apart.

Most scientists now believe that about 15 billion years ago all the matter in the universe was packed tightly together into a small mass. It was incredibly dense and hot. Our universe began when this fireball exploded in what is now called the **Big Bang.** Bits of matter, heat waves, and blazing light shot out. Within minutes of the explosion, atomic particles came together to make the gases hydrogen and helium.

By about one billion years after the Big Bang, huge gas clouds started to pull together under the action of gravity. The first stars were formed in clumps, like large clusters of small galaxies. Clumps joined together to make larger galaxies. About 9 billion years later our Sun and solar system, including the Earth, were formed. Ever since that first gigantic explosion, our universe has been spreading out.

Gravity is slowing down the expansion of the universe because all the galaxies pull on each other. No one is quite sure whether the galaxies will continue to race apart for ever. Then the original hydrogen would finally be used up in making new stars. The last stars would shine and go out and our universe would become cold and lifeless. Another possibility is that the force of gravity might slow the galaxies down enough to stop them. Then they would fall back together to form another super hot, extremely dense mass of material. It would expand in a new big bang and the universe would start all over again.

Questions

1. What is a light-year? Why do astronomers use light years instead of kilometres as a unit of distance?

2. What is a galaxy?

3. What is the name of the galaxy to which our Sun belongs?

4. How are the light and high temperatures in the Sun or some other star produced?

5. What are sunspots and what have scientists learnt about the Sun's rotation by studying the movement of sunspots?

6. Stars eventually burn out and die. Some of the stars we see in the night sky now may no longer exist. Why is this?

7. What is a constellation?

8. Why would people living in the southern hemisphere not see the same constellations that we do?

9. Name a few space probes. How do they work?

10. Why should we not look directly at the Sun?

11. Which constellations can be seen all the year round?

12. Why are reflecting telescopes (rather than refracting telescopes) used when a more powerful telescope is needed to study the stars.

13. Light travels at 300,000 km in a second. Can you work out how far light travels in a year?

14. In your own words, explain what the 'Big Bang' theory is, and what evidence scientists have that it occurred.

15. What are radio telescopes? Why are they used?

1. Every month certain newspapers publish notes and maps of the night sky. Cut out one of these maps and mount it on a sheet of card. Hold the chart in front of you and make sure that 'North' on the chart is pointing towards the north. Use a compass if you are not sure which direction north is. Use the chart to help you identify the positions of the main stars, constellations, and planets.

2. Keep an 'Outer Space Diary'. In it, place newspaper and magazine articles and photographs of important discoveries in outer space as they occur. Write against each article and picture the date when it was published.

OXFORD
UNIVERSITY PRESS

Glossary

active transport	the movement of substances such as mineral salts through a membrane, from a low to a high concentration
adaptation	the process by which an organism becomes suited to its environment
addictive	something, such as a drug or tobacco, which cannot easily be given up
aerobic respiration	respiration which uses air or oxygen
alveoli (singular: alveolus)	the tiny air-sacs at the end of each bronchiole in the lungs through which oxygen diffuses in and carbon dioxide diffuses out
ammeter	an instrument for measuring electric current
ampere (A)	the unit of electric current
amplitude	the height of a wave from its peak to its mean rest position. The size of the amplitude shows how much energy is carried by the wave and how loud the sound is.
anion	a negatively charged ion
antibody	a chemical produced by certain cells in the body which kills or weakens germs, thereby protecting the body against certain diseases
anus	the opening at the lower end of the digestive system from which solid waste leaves the body
artery	a blood vessel that carries blood under pressure away from the heart to a part of the body
asexual	without sex; not involving the two sexes
atrium (plural atria)	one of the two upper chambers of the heart
atom	the smallest part of an element that can exist
atomic number	the number of protons in the nucleus of each atom of an element
battery	a number of electric cells joined together
Big Bang	a theory which suggests that the universe was formed from an extremely dense mass of material which exploded about 15 billion years ago
bile	a greenish liquid made in the liver and passed into the small intestine, where it helps to digest fats
biodegradable	describes any substance which can be broken down by the natural processes of decay
black hole	a region in space where gravity is so strong that even light cannot escape. It is thought to be formed after a supernova.
boiling	the rapid change in state from a liquid to a gas or vapour
bond	a force of attraction between atoms inside a molecule or crystal
bone marrow	soft tissue that fills the centre of spongy bone. Bone marrow is where red and white blood cells and platelets are produced.
bronchus	a branch of the trachea or windpipe leading to a lung
bronchiole	one of the end air tubes in the lungs
bulb	a short, thick, underground bud with scaly leaves which contain stored food (e.g. daffodil, onion)
capillary	a small, thin-walled blood vessel which carries materials to and from cells
carpel	the female sex organ of a flower
catalyst	a substance which increases the rate of a chemical reaction without itself undergoing any permanent change

Glossary

cation	a positively charged ion
cell	the basic unit of living things. All organisms are made up of one or more cells. A source of electric current, usually produced by chemical changes.
cell sap	a liquid found in the plant cell vacuole. It contains substances like water and dissolved sugars and mineral salts.
chemical change	another name for an irreversible change
chemical formula	shows the number and kinds of atoms contained in each molecule
chemical reaction	the process in which new substances are created by rearrangement of atoms or molecules
chemical equation	a summary of the reactants involved and the products formed during a chemical reaction
cilia	minute hair-like projections from the surface of certain cells. Cilia flick back and forth causing surrounding liquids to move.
circuit	a continuous conducting path along which electricity can flow
circuit diagram	a shorthand way of showing how to connect the components in a circuit
clotting	when the blood forms a solid mass on contact with air in order to seal a cut or graze
colour subtraction	the mixing together of paints, dyes or pigments which have colour because they absorb some of the components of white light and reflect the rest
combustion	the burning of a substance in oxygen to form new substance(s). Heat and sometimes light energy are given off during combustion.
community	a group of different organisms living together in a habitat
companion cell	an elongated cell situated alongside a sieve tube in the phloem
competition	the struggle that living things have against each other, such as for food, space, places to breed, etc. in order to survive
compound	a substance made up of two or more elements combined by a chemical reaction
conduction	the movement or transfer of heat or electricity through a material, without any visible flow or movement of the material taking place
concave lens	a lens whose surface curves inwards and which refracts light outwards so that it diverges, or is spread out
cones	cells which form part of the retina of the eye. Cones are sensitive to bright light and to red, green, and blue light.
consumer	an organism that does not make its own food
convection	the transfer or movement of heat through a gas or liquid which involves movement of the gas or liquid
convection current	the flow of heat through a liquid or a gas
convex lens	a lens which is thicker at the centre than at the outsides. It can produce a real image on a surface or a large virtual image when used as a magnifying glass.
compression	the act of pressing or squeezing together
conductor	a substance which carries heat or electricity well
constellation	a group of stars in the sky which form a fixed pattern in relation to each other, as viewed from Earth
corm	a short, thick stem in which food is stored (e.g. crocus)

OXFORD
UNIVERSITY PRESS

cotyledon	a seed leaf containing a store of food for the developing seedling
covalent bond	a chemical bond formed by the sharing between atoms of their outermost electrons
critical angle	the smallest angle of incidence at which total internal reflection occurs
cross-pollination	the transfer of pollen from the anther to the stigma of a flower on a different plant of the same species
current	a flow of electric charge through a conductor
dam	a barrier built across a large river to hold back the water
decibel (dB)	the unit for measuring the loudness of sound
deciduous	refers to a tree which loses all its leaves in winter
decomposer	an organism, such as a bacterium or fungus, that feeds off dead plants or animals
desalination	the removal of salt from sea water
detritivore	an animal that feeds on the dead decomposing remains of plants and animals and breaks them down into simpler substances
diaphragm	a sheet of muscle situated below the lungs
diffusion	the movement of molecules from a region of higher concentration to a region of lower concentration
digestion	the breakdown of large molecules of food into smaller molecules that can be absorbed into the blood
disperse	to scatter
distillation	the separation of a liquid from a mixture by heating until the liquid boils and then cooling and condensing the vapour
dormant	resting or sleeping
earth leakage circuit-breaker (ELCB)	an electromagnetic switch which turns off the power if the leakage of current flowing through the earth wire is greater than its rating
echo	a reflection of sound waves made by an object so that a weaker version is heard after the original
echolocation	a way of detecting objects using sound waves and echoes
ecosystem	a system formed by plants, animals, and the non-living environment interacting with one another
electric charge	whether an object has an overall positive or negative charge
electric current	the rate of flow of electric charges
electrolysis	chemical reactions brought about by an electric current passing through a liquid or molten solid
electromagnetic radiation	waves of energy that can travel at the speed of light through space and matter from the Sun, stars, and galaxies to reach us. It consists of radio waves, microwaves, infra-red rays, light rays, ultra-violet rays, X-rays, and gamma rays
electron	a tiny negatively charged particle which moves in orbit around the nucleus of an atom
electron shell	a group of electrons that share the same 'orbit' around the nucleus of an atom. The further an electron shell is from the nucleus, the higher its energy level
electroplating	coating objects with a thin layer of metal by the process of electrolysis

Glossary

element	a substance which cannot be broken down into simpler substances by any ordinary chemical method
embryo	the stage of development between a fertilized egg-cell and the newly formed organism
endosperm	a mass of dry, powdery cells inside a seed which store food for use when the seed germinates.
endothermic reaction	a chemical reaction during which heat is taken in from the surroundings
energy	in science, energy is the ability to do work. There are various forms of energy.
enzyme	a special kind of protein made by living things which brings about or speeds up certain chemical reactions without being used up itself
exothermic reaction	a chemical reaction during which heat is given out to the surroundings
extinct	not existing any more
faeces	waste matter produced by animals that is mainly undigested and unabsorbed food
fertilization	the fusion, or joining, of male and female sex cells during sexual reproduction
fertilizer	any substance that is added to the soil to improve its fertility and make plants grow better
fibrinogen	a protein substance in the blood plasma which hardens on contact with the air and helps to form a clot over a cut or wound
filament	the thin wire inside a light bulb; the stalk which holds the anther in a stamen
filter	a coloured film which absorbs all light falling on it, except for the colour of the filter itself which it allows to pass through
food chain	a series of organisms through which energy in transferred in the form of food
food web	a network made up of two or more inter-related food chains
fractional distillation	a method of separating mixtures of liquids by distillation because of their differing boiling points
frequency	the number of complete vibrations per second in a wave motion
fruit	a structure which develops from the wall of the ovary of a plant after fertilization. It contains the seeds.
fuse	a short, thin piece of wire which heats up and melts when the current flowing through it exceeds a certain amount
galaxy	a giant collection of many millions of stars
gastric juice	digestive juice produced by the walls of the stomach. It begins the digestion of proteins and contains hydrochloric acid which kills any germs that have been swallowed.
germination	the early stages in the growth of a seed to form a seedling
glacier	a moving river of ice
global warming	the gradual change in the world's climate brought about by the greenhouse effect.
greenhouse effect	the warming effect produced when heat energy is trapped in the Earth's atmosphere by gases such as carbon dioxide, methane, and oxides of nitrogen
gullet (or oesophagus)	a narrow tube with strong muscles in its walls. The muscles contract in a wave-like manner that pushes food down the oesophagus into the stomach.
habitat	a place where an organism lives and reproduces
haemoglobin	the compound in red blood cells which is made up of iron and protein that combines with, and carries, oxygen

OXFORD
UNIVERSITY PRESS

heat	a form of energy which flows from a region of higher temperature to a region of lower temperature
hertz (Hz)	the unit of frequency
hibernate	To sleep for a long time during cold weather
hormone	a chemical produced in small amounts in animals which helps to control processes such as growth and reproduction
humus	the dark brown organic part of the soil produced by the decay of plant and animal remains by decomposing organisms. Humus is rich in nutrients and helps keep the soil moist.
hydrocarbon	a compound that contains only carbon and hydrogen atoms
image	a picture of an object that can be produced by a mirror, lens, or an optical system
infrared radiation	the way in which heat energy is transferred from a hotter to a colder place without a medium such as air or water
insulator	a substance which is a poor conductor of heat or electricity
intercostal muscles	muscles between the ribs that contract to raise the ribcage when breathing in
ion	a charged particle formed when an atom (or group of atoms) gains or loses one or more electrons
ionic bond	a chemical bond formed by the transfer of one or more electrons from the outer shell of a metal atom to the outer shell of a non-metal atom
irrigation	supplying land with water so that crops can grow
isotopes	atoms of the same element with different numbers of neutrons and so different mass numbers.
kilowatt-hour	the electrical energy used at a rate of 1000 watts or one kilowatt per hour
laser	a device that produces a beam of high-energy light
laxative	a medicine that causes your bowels or rectum to empty
lens	a piece of transparent material with curved surfaces which bends or refracts light
lenticel	special pores that let gases enter the bark of a tree to reach the cells inside
light-year	the distance travelled by light in one year
longitudinal wave	a progressive wave in which the vibrations are along the line of the direction in which the sound wave is travelling
luminous	describes an object that gives out light of its own
magnify	to make larger
mammal	a warm-blooded vertebrate animal, the female of which produces milk to feed its young
melting	the change that occurs when a solid turns into a liquid when it is heated
migration	a seasonal movement by an animal to a more favourable environment
milky way	the galaxy to which our Sun belongs
mineral salts	substances containing chemical elements essential to the health of a plant or animal
molecule	two or more atoms chemically combined together. The atoms in the molecule may be of the same kind, e.g. in an oxygen molecule, a hydrogen molecule, and a nitrogen molecule. The atoms may also be different, e.g. in a water molecule and a carbon dioxide molecule.
mucus	a slippery liquid produced by certain cells of the body
neutron	an uncharged particle in the nucleus of an atom

Glossary

neutron star	an extremely small and dense object in space formed after a supernova
noise	unpleasant or unwanted sound
non-reversible	cannot be reversed
normal line	an imaginary line at right angles to a surface where a light ray strikes it
nuclear fission	the splitting of an atom into two or more parts
nuclear fusion	the joining together of the nuclei of light elements, e.g. hydrogen, to form more massive elements and to release energy
nucleus	the part of the cell that controls all the activities in the cell. It contains chromosomes. The central part of an atom, consisting of protons and neutrons
oesophagus	a narrow muscular tube through which food moves from the mouth to the stomach
opaque	describes an object that does not allow light to pass through
oscilloscope	a special device, similar to a television tube, which shows the changing voltage of an electrical signal as a curved line or graph, on a screen. It can show changes in electric currents, brain waves, as well as sound waves.
osmosis	the movement of water from a dilute to a more concentrated solution by diffusion across a semipermeable membrane
pancreas	an organ situated between the stomach and the small intestine which produces digestive enzymes
parallel circuit	a circuit formed when the components are arranged so that there is more than one path for the current to take.
petal	a coloured flap that often helps a flower to attract animal pollinators
phloem	tiny tubes in a flowering plant that carry food from the leaves to other parts of the plant
physical change	another name for a reversible change
pitch	the sensation of how high or how low a sound is
plasma	the pale yellow liquid part of the blood which is mainly made of water, which carries digested food, carbon dioxide, hormones, and dissolved waste substances
platelet	tiny fragments of cells that help the blood to clot if the skin is cut
plumule	the first shoot or stem which grows from a seed as it begins to germinate
pollen tube	a tube which grows from a pollen grain and into an ovule or egg-cell
pollination	the transfer of pollen grains from stamens to stigmas
pollution	the altering of the balance of the natural world by chemicals, litter, sewage, and other agents
polymer	a compound with large molecules that contain many small molecules linked together
primary colours	the primary colours of light are red, blue, and green which can be mixed to give white
prism	a transparent triangular block that splits light into a spectrum
producer	a green plant which makes food using light energy, water, and carbon dioxide during the process of photosynthesis
product	the chemical(s) formed after a chemical reaction
prominence	a blazing burst of gas that comes from the surface of the Sun, shoots up hundreds or even thousands of kilometres into space, and then loops back down again
protease	an enzyme which breaks down proteins into smaller molecules such as peptides and amino acids
proton	a positively charged particle in the nucleus of an atom

OXFORD
UNIVERSITY PRESS

pupa	a stage in the life cycle of an insect during which it changes into the adult form of the insect
pyramid of biomass	a diagram that shows the relative mass of living things at different stages of a food chain
pyramid of numbers	a diagram that shows the relative numbers of living things at different stages of a food chain
radiant heat	the flow of heat in the form of infra-red rays
radiation	the movement or transfer of energy through a vacuum in the form of electromagnetic rays. A hot body can transfer heat energy to a cooler body through a vacuum by means of radiation.
radicle	the root which emerges from a seed at the beginning of germination
radioisotope	a radioactive form of an element
reactant	one of the chemical substances which takes part in a chemical reaction
red blood cell	one of the disc-shaped cells containing haemoglobin, which transports oxygen from the lungs to the body tissues
reflecting telescope	a telescope which uses a concave mirror and an eyepiece to produce a magnified image of a distant object
refracting telescope	a telescope which uses convex lenses to produce a magnified image of a distant object
refraction	the change in the speed and direction of light when it passes from one transparent material to another
refractive index (RI)	an index that shows by how much a pair of materials refracts light. The higher the refractive index, the more light will be refracted.
reproduce	to produce offspring
reservoir	a large tank or artificial lake where water is stored before it is used
resistance	the degree to which a substance resists an electric current
resistor	an electrical component that has a particular resistance
respiration	the release of energy in living organisms which occurs when food molecules are broken down
retina	the light-sensitive layer of cells at the back of the eye
reversible reaction	a chemical reaction in which the products can be made to react together to produce the reactants.
rods	cells in the retina of the eye which respond to dim light
root cap	the thickened layer of cells which protects the tip of a root
root hair	a single-celled, hair-like structure found near the tip of a root. It absorbs water and dissolved mineral salts from the soil.
root pressure	the pressure that causes water to pass up the xylem from the living cells of a plant root
runner	a stem which grows horizontally from the plant and forms roots for new plants where it touches the ground (e.g. strawberry)
satellite	a body that orbits another larger body in space under the influence of its gravitational field
sewage	waste matter carried away in drains
scavenger	an animal that feeds on dead organisms
secondary colours	colours of light that can be produced by mixing two primary colours
seed	a structure containing an embryo plant and food store that enables a plant to reproduce itself
self-pollination	the transfer of pollen from an anther to a stigma of the same flower

Glossary

semi-permeable membrane	a membrane which allows molecules of water (solvent) to pass though, but not the molecules of most dissolved substances (solutes)
sepal	a small protective leaf-like structure found around a flower bud
series circuit	a circuit formed when the components are arranged so that there is a single path for the current to take
sexual reproduction	reproduction that usually involves two parents both of which produce sex cells. These sex cells fuse together and the resulting cell eventually forms a new organism
small intestine	the part of the digestive system between the stomach and large intestine. Digestion of food is completed in the first part of the small intestine, absorption of the digested food takes place in the second part.
solar flare	a burst of hot material that shoots out from the Sun into space
solar system	the Sun and the eight planets, including Earth that orbit the Sun. The solar system also includes asteroids, moons, and comets.
sound wave	compressions and rarefactions caused in a medium when it is disturbed by a vibrating object
spectrum	the band of colours formed when light is split by a prism
stamen	one of the male reproductive organs of a flower. The anthers of the stamens produce pollen grains.
star	a body in space which generates its own heat and light from nuclear fusion within its core
states of matter	the three forms in which matter can exist: solid, liquid, and gas
stoma (plural stomata)	one of the many tiny pores in the outer layer of plant stems and on the underside of leaves
succession	an orderly change in the species living in a community over a period of time
sunspot	a dark area on the surface of the Sun where the temperature is lower
supernova	an immense explosion produced when an old and very massive star has used up its fuel for nuclear fusion and collapses under its own gravity
temperature	a measure of how hot or cold a body is
terminal	one of the parts of a cell or battery to which the wires must be connected in a circuit
thermal imaging camera	a camera which can detect or photograph the heat radiating from hot objects
thermometer	an instrument used for measuring temperature
total internal reflection	the complete reflection of light at a boundary between two materials
trachea	the windpipe
translocation	the transport of the products of photosynthesis within a plant
translucent	describes an object or material that allows some light to pass through, but scatters the light. Objects placed behind any translucent material cannot be seen clearly.
transparent	describes an object or material that allows light to pass through so that objects behind can be seen clearly
transpiration	the process whereby plants lose water by evaporation
transpiration stream	the flow of water up the stem of a plant as a result of transpiration
transverse wave	a progressive wave in which the vibrations are at right angles to the direction in which the wave is travelling
tuber	a swollen underground stem which acts as a food store and which produces buds for new

	plants (e.g. potato, dahlia)
ultrasound	high-frequency sound that is above the range that humans can hear
ultrasonic	describes a sound that is above the range of human hearing
universe	the universe is all the matter, energy, and space that exists
vaccine	a preparation containing dead or weakened viruses which is used to prevent diseases such as polio, tetanus, and measles
vacuum	empty space; without any matter in it
vacuum flask	a container designed to minimise heat transfer. It is used to keep hot liquids hot, while cold liquids remain cold.
valency	the combining power of an element
valve	a device used to control the flow of a gas or liquid
vegetative propagation	a type of asexual reproduction or vegetative reproduction in which part of the parent plant is able to develop into a new plant
vein	a blood vessel that carries blood black to the heart from other parts of the body
ventricle	one of the two lower chambers of the human heart
vibrate	to move or cause movement—to and fro or up and down
vibration	the action of moving quickly to and fro or up and down
villi	tiny finger-like structures on the inner surface of the small intestine. These occur in millions, greatly increasing the surface area available to absorb digested food into the blood.
virus	a microorganism which consists of a core of DNA surrounded by a protein coat. All viruses are parasites and cause diseases in plants, animals, and some bacteria.
vocal cords	strips of flesh near the top of the trachea or windpipe which can be stretched by muscles to produce different sounds
volt	a unit for measuring the strength of an electric current
voltmeter	an instrument for measuring voltage
water cycle	the natural process by which water is recycled between the Earth, the atmosphere, and living things
wavelength	the distance between two identical points on a wave
white blood cell	a type of cell found in the blood which engulfs germs and fights infection
wilted	a state when a plant has lost more water by transpiration than it can replace by osmosis
windpipe (trachea)	a tube through which air is drawn into the lungs
xylem	tiny tubes in a flowering plant that carry water and dissolved mineral salts from the roots to all parts of the plant

Book **Piracy** and **Plagiarism** are **Crimes.** Beware of both!

Look out for the new security label whenever you purchase an Oxford textbook or supplementary reader. Labels with the features shown below are proof of genuine Oxford books.

- An iridescent circle with OUP written on it is featured on the left side of the label. The circle changes colour from orange to green when viewed from different angles.
- The labels tear if peeled from the book cover.
- The labels have security cut marks on the right and the left side to prevent them from being peeled off and reused.
- The word 'ORIGINAL' appears when the area under 'SCRATCH HERE' is rubbed with a coin.
- The words 'GENUINE' written in very small print become visible when viewed under a magnifying glass.

Do not accept the book if the label is missing, has been torn or tampered with, the colour on the security label does not change or the word 'ORIGINAL' does not appear upon rubbing the area with a coin.

Pirated books can be recognized by:

- inferior production quality
- low-grade paper
- variations in texture and colour
- poor print quality
- blurred text and images
- poor binding and trimming
- substandard appearance of the book

If you suspect that you are being sold a pirated book without the security label, please contact:

Oxford University Press, No. 38, Sector 15, Korangi Industrial Area, P.O. Box No. 8214, Karachi-74900, Pakistan.
Tel.: (92-21) 35071580-86 • Fax: (92-21) 35055071-72 • E-mail: central.marketing.pk@oup.com

Website: www.oup.com/pk • Find us on facebook